Authors

James Flood
Jan E. Hasbrouck
James V. Hoffman
Diane Lapp
Donna Lubcker
Angela Shelf Medearis
Scott Paris
Steven Stahl
Josefina Villamil Tinajero
Karen D. Wood

Students with print disabilities may be eligible to obtain an accessible, audio version of the pupil edition of this textbook. Please call Recording for the Blind & Dyslexic at 1-800-221-4792 for complete information.

Macmillan/McGraw-Hill
A Division of The ***McGraw-Hill*** *Companies*

Published by Macmillan/McGraw-Hill, a division of The McGraw-Hill Companies, Inc., Two Penn Plaza, NY, NY 10121

Printed in the United States of America ISBN 0-02-188555-9/K 3 4 5 6 7 8 9 071/043 04 03 02

New York Farmington

UNIT 1

My World

Aa, Bb 6
Left to Right 7
Cc, Dd 8
Use Illustrations 9
Ee, Ff 10
High-Frequency Word: *the* 11
Gg, Hh 12
Story: "The House" 13
REVIEW Use Illustrations 15
Ii, Jj, Kk 16
REVIEW High-Frequency Word: *the* 17

Ll, Mm, Nn 18
First, Next, Last 19
Oo, Pp, Qq 20
Sequence of Events 21
Rr, Ss, Tt 22
High-Frequency Word: *a* 23
Uu, Vv, Ww 24
Story: "A Present" 25
REVIEW Sequence of Events 27
Xx, Yy, Zz 28
REVIEW High-Frequency Words: *a, the* 29

Initial /n/*n* 30
Colors 31
Final /n/*n* 32
REVIEW Use Illustrations 33
REVIEW /n/*n* 34
High-Frequency Word: *my* 35
REVIEW Letter Identification 36
Story: "My School" 37
REVIEW Use Illustrations 39
REVIEW Letter Identification 40
REVIEW High-Frequency Words: *my, the, a* 41

Initial /a/*a* 42
REVIEW Colors 43
Medial /a/*a* 44
REVIEW Sequence of Events 45
REVIEW /a/*a* 46
High-Frequency Word: *that* 47
Blending with Short *a* 48
Story: "Nan" 49
REVIEW Sequence of Events 51
REVIEW Blending with Short *a* 52
REVIEW High-Frequency Words: *that, my, the, a* 53

REVIEW Initial /n/*n*, /a/*a* 54
REVIEW Colors; Left to Right; First, Next, Last 55
REVIEW Final /n/*n*; Medial /a/*a* 56
REVIEW Use Illustrations 57
REVIEW /n/*n*, /a/*a* 58
REVIEW High-Frequency Words: *the, a, my, that* 59
REVIEW Blending with Short *a* 60
Story: "That Nan!" 61
REVIEW Sequence of Events 63
REVIEW Blending with Short *a* 64
REVIEW High-Frequency Words: *the, a, my, that* 65

UNIT 2

All Kinds of Friends

Initial /d/*d* .66
Numbers .67
Final /d/*d* .68
Story Details .69
REVIEW /d/*d* .70
High-Frequency Word: *and* .71
REVIEW Blending with Short *a* .72
Story: "Dan and Dad" .73
Story Details .75
REVIEW Blending with Short *a* .76
REVIEW High-Frequency Words: *and, my, a* .77

Initial /s/*s* .78
REVIEW Numbers .79
REVIEW Initial /s/*s* .80
Classify and Categorize .81
REVIEW /s/*s*, /d/*d* .82
High-Frequency Word: *I* .83
REVIEW Blending with Short *a* .84
Story: "Dad, Dan, and I" .85
REVIEW Classify and Categorize .87
REVIEW Blending with Short *a* .88
REVIEW High-Frequency Words: *I, and, my* .89

Initial /m/*m* .90
Shapes: Circle, Triangle .91
Final /m/*m* .92
Story Details .93
REVIEW /m/*m* .94
High-Frequency Word: *is* .95
REVIEW Blending with Short *a* .96
Story: "I Am Sam!" .97
REVIEW Story Details .99
REVIEW Blending with Short *a* .100
REVIEW High-Frequency Words: *is, I, and, that* .101

Initial /i/*i* .102
REVIEW Shapes: Square, Rectangle .103
Medial /i/*i* .104
REVIEW Classify and Categorize .105
REVIEW /i/*i* .106
High-Frequency Word: *said* .107
Blending with Short *i* .108
Story: "Sid Said" .109
REVIEW Classify and Categorize .111
REVIEW Blending with Short *i, a* .112
REVIEW High-Frequency Words: *said, I, is* .113

REVIEW Initial /d/*d*, /s/*s*, /m/*m* .114
REVIEW Shapes and Numbers .115
REVIEW Final /d/*d*, /m/*m* .116
REVIEW Story Details .117
REVIEW /d/*d*, /m/*m*, /s/*s* .118
High-Frequency Words: *and, I, is, said* .119
REVIEW Blending with Short *i, a* .120
Story: "Is Sam Mad?" .121
REVIEW Classify and Categorize .123
REVIEW Blending with Short *i, a* .124
REVIEW High-Frequency Words: *and, I, is, said* .125

UNIT 3

Time to Shine

Initial /t/*t* 126
Opposites 127
REVIEW Final /t/*t* 128
Fantasy and Reality 129
REVIEW /t/*t* 130
High-Frequency Word: *we* 131
REVIEW Blending with Short *a, i* 132
Story: "That Tam!" 133
REVIEW Fantasy and Reality 135
REVIEW Blending with Short *a, i* 136
REVIEW High-Frequency Words: *we, said, the* 137

Initial /k/*c* 138
REVIEW Opposites 139
REVIEW Initial /k/*c* 140
Make Predictions 141
REVIEW Initial /k/*c*, /t/*t* 142
High-Frequency Word: *are* 143
REVIEW Blending with Short *a* 144
Story: "Nat Is My Cat" 145
REVIEW Make Predictions 147
REVIEW Blending with Short *a, i* 148
REVIEW High-Frequency Words: *are, we, is* 149

Initial /o/*o* 150
Above, On, Below 151
Medial /o/*o* 152
REVIEW Fantasy and Reality 153
REVIEW /o/*o* 154
High-Frequency Word: *you* 155
Blending with Short *o* 156
Story: "On a Dot" 157
REVIEW Fantasy and Reality 159
REVIEW Blending with Short *o, i* 160
REVIEW High-Frequency Words: *you, are, that, my* 161

Initial /f/*f* 162
Top, Middle, Bottom 163
REVIEW Initial /f/*f* 164
REVIEW Make Predictions 165
REVIEW /f/*f*, /k/*c* 166
High-Frequency Word: *have* 167
REVIEW Blending with Short *a, i* 168
Story: "We Fit!" 169
REVIEW Make Predictions 171
REVIEW Blending with Short *a, i, o* 172
REVIEW High-Frequency Words: *have, we, you, are, is* 173

REVIEW Initial /t/*t*, /k/*c*, /f/*f* 174
REVIEW Opposites; Top, Middle, Bottom 175
REVIEW Final /t/*t* 176
REVIEW Fantasy and Reality 177
REVIEW /t/*t*, /k/*c*, /f/*f* 178
REVIEW High-Frequency Words: *we, are, you, have* 179
REVIEW Blending with Short *o* 180
Story: "A Tin Can" 181
REVIEW Make Predictions 183
REVIEW Blending with Short *a, i, o* 184
REVIEW High Frequency Words: *we, are, you, have* 185

UNIT 4

I Wonder

Initial /r/*r* 186
On, Off 187
REVIEW Initial /r/*r* 188
Main Idea 189
REVIEW /r/*r*, /f/*f* 190
High-Frequency Word: *to* 191
REVIEW Blending with Short *a, i, o* 192
Story: "You Are IT!" 193
REVIEW Main Idea 195
REVIEW Blending with Short *a, i, o* 196
REVIEW High-Frequency Words: *to, the, that* 197

Initial /p/*p* 198
Inside, Outside 199
Final /p/*p* 200
Compare and Contrast 201
REVIEW /p/*p* 202
High-Frequency Word: *me* 203
REVIEW Blending with Short *a, i, o* 204
Story: "Is It You?" 205
REVIEW Compare and Contrast 207
REVIEW Blending with Short *a, i, o* 208
REVIEW High-Frequency Words: *me, to, you* 209

Initial /l/*l* 210
Over, Under 211
REVIEW Initial /l/*l* 212
REVIEW Main Idea 213
REVIEW /l/*l*, /p/*p* 214
High-Frequency Word: *go* 215
REVIEW Blending with Short *a, i, o* 216
Story: "Go, Lad, Go!" 217
REVIEW Main Idea 219
REVIEW Blending with Short *a, i, o* 220
REVIEW High-Frequency Words: *go, to, me, you* 221

Initial /u/*u* 222
Up, Down 223
Medial /u/*u* 224
REVIEW Compare and Contrast 225
REVIEW /u/*u* 226
High-Frequency Word: *do* 227
Blending with Short *u* 228
Story: "Mud Fun" 229
REVIEW Compare and Contrast 231
REVIEW Blending with Short *u, o* 232
REVIEW High-Frequency Words: *do, go, I, and, me* 233

REVIEW Initial /r/*r*, /p/*p*, /l/*l* 234
REVIEW Positional Terms 235
REVIEW Final /p/*p* 236
REVIEW Main Idea 237
REVIEW /r/*r*, /p/*p*, /l/*l* 238
REVIEW High-Frequency Words: *to, me, go, do* 239
REVIEW Blending with Short *u* 240
Story: "Ron and Me" 241
REVIEW Compare and Contrast 243
REVIEW Blending with Short *u, o, i* 244
REVIEW High-Frequency Words: *to, me, go, do* 245

UNIT 5

Let's Work It Out

Initial /k/*k* 246
Naming Words 247
Final /k/*ck* 248
Story Structure 249
REVIEW /k/*k*, /k/*ck* 250
High-Frequency Word: *for* 251
REVIEW Blending with Short *a, i, o, u* 252
Story: "Tom Is Sick" 253
REVIEW Story Structure 255
REVIEW Blending with Short *a, i, o, u* 256
REVIEW High-Frequency Words: *for, you, me* 257

Initial /g/*g* 258
REVIEW Naming Words 259
Final /g/*g* 260
Summarize 261
REVIEW /g/*g* 262
High-Frequency Word: *he* 263
REVIEW Blending with Short *a, i, o, u* 264
Story: "He is Pug" 265
REVIEW Summarize 267
REVIEW Blending with Short *a, i, o, u* 268
REVIEW High-Frequency Words: *he, for, is* 269

Initial /e/*e* 270
Action Words 271
Medial /e/*e* 272
REVIEW Story Structure 273
REVIEW /e/*e* 274
High-Frequency Word: *she* 275
Blending with Short *e* 276
Story: "A Pet for Ken" 277
REVIEW Story Structure 279
REVIEW Blending with Short *e, u* 280
REVIEW High-Frequency Words: *she, he, for, is* 281

Initial /b/*b* 282
REVIEW Action Words 283
Final /b/*b* 284
REVIEW Summarize 285
REVIEW /b/*b* 286
High-Frequency Word: *has* 287
REVIEW Blending with Short *a, e, i, o, u* 288
Story: "A Big Bug" 289
REVIEW Summarize 291
REVIEW Blending with Short *a, e, i o, u* 292
REVIEW High-Frequency Words: *has, he, she, me, for* 293

REVIEW Initial /k/*k*, /g/*g*, /b/*b* 294
REVIEW Naming and Action Words 295
REVIEW Final /k/*ck*, /g/*g*, /b/*b* 296
REVIEW Story Structure 297
REVIEW /k/*k*, /k/*ck*, /g/*g*, /b/*b* 298
REVIEW High-Frequency Words: *for, he, she, has* 299
REVIEW Blending with Short *a, e, i, o, u* 300
Story: "Pup and Cat" 301
REVIEW Summarize 303
REVIEW Blending with Short *a, e, i, o, u* 304
REVIEW High-Frequency Words: *for, he, she, has* 305

UNIT 6

Choices

Initial /h/*h* 306
REVIEW Shapes: Circle, Triangle 307
REVIEW Initial /h/*h* 308
Cause and Effect 309
REVIEW /h/*h*, /b/*b* 310
High-Frequency Word: *with* 311
REVIEW Blending with Short *a, e, i, o, u* 312
Story: "Hop with a Hog" 313
REVIEW Cause and Effect 315
REVIEW Blending with Short *a, e, i, o, u* 316
REVIEW High-Frequency Words: *with, go, the, me, and* 317

Initial /w/*w* 318
REVIEW Shapes: Square, Rectangle 319
REVIEW Initial /w/*w* 320
Make Inferences 321
REVIEW /w/*w*, /h/*h* 322
High-Frequency Word: *was* 323
REVIEW Blending with Short *a, e, i, o, u* 324
Story: "We Win!" 325
REVIEW Make Inferences 327
REVIEW Blending with Short *a, e, i, o, u* 328
REVIEW High-Frequency Words: *was, with, I, he, she* 329

Initial /v/*v* 330
REVIEW Categories 331
Final /ks/*x* 332
REVIEW Cause and Effect 333
REVIEW /v/*v*, /ks/*x* 334
High-Frequency Word: *see* 335
REVIEW Blending with Short *a, e, i, o, u* 336
Story: "The Vet Van" 337
REVIEW Cause and Effect 339
REVIEW Blending with Short *a, e, i, o, u* 340
REVIEW High-Frequency Words: *see, was, is, do, we, are, with* 341

Initial /kw/*qu* 342
REVIEW Categories 343
Initial /j/*j* 344
REVIEW Make Inferences 345
Initial /y/*y* and /z/*z* 346
High-Frequency Word: *of* 347
REVIEW Blending with Short *a, e, i, o, u* 348
Story: "Jen and Yip" 349
REVIEW Make Inferences 351
REVIEW Blending with Short *a, e, i, o, u* 352
REVIEW High-Frequency Words: *of, see, that, my* 353

REVIEW Blending with Short *a, e, i, o, u* 354
REVIEW Shapes and Categories 355
REVIEW Blending with Short *a, e, i, o, u* 356
REVIEW Cause and Effect 357
REVIEW Blending with Short *a, e, i, o, u* 358
REVIEW High-Frequency Words: *with, was, see, of* 359
REVIEW Blending with Short *a, e, i, o, u* 360
Story: "Zack and Jan" 361
REVIEW Make Inferences 363
REVIEW Blending with Short *a, e, i, o, u* 364
REVIEW High-Frequency Words: *with, was, see, of* 365

Aa Bb

Name ______________________________

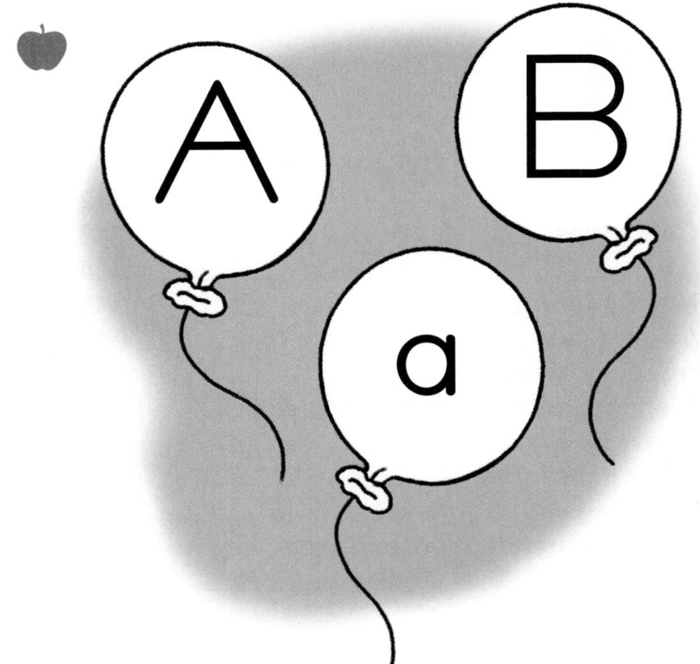

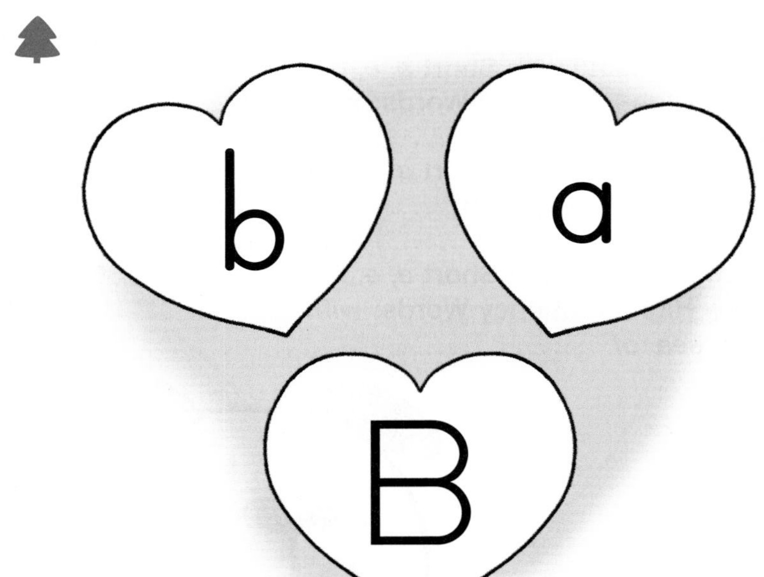

Name the letters in each box. • Color the pictures that show the uppercase and lowercase forms of the same letter.

Name ______________________________

Draw a line from left to right to connect the person with the place where he or she is going.

Cc Dd

Name________________________________

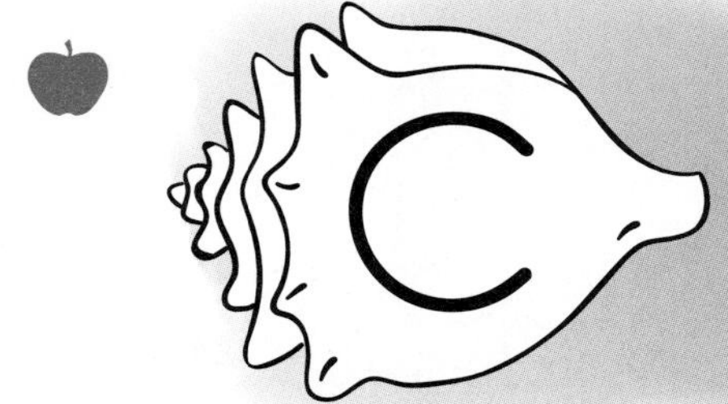

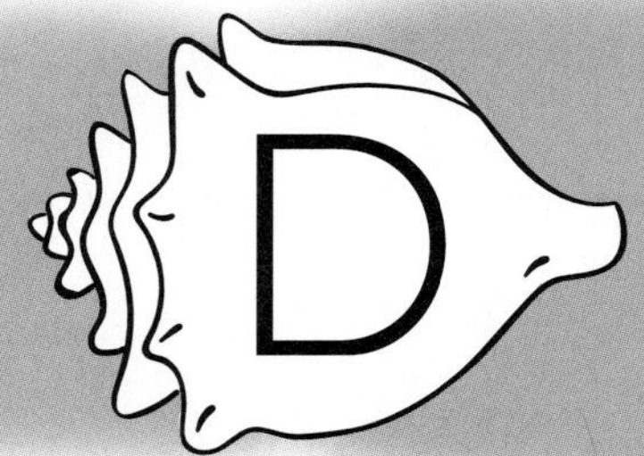

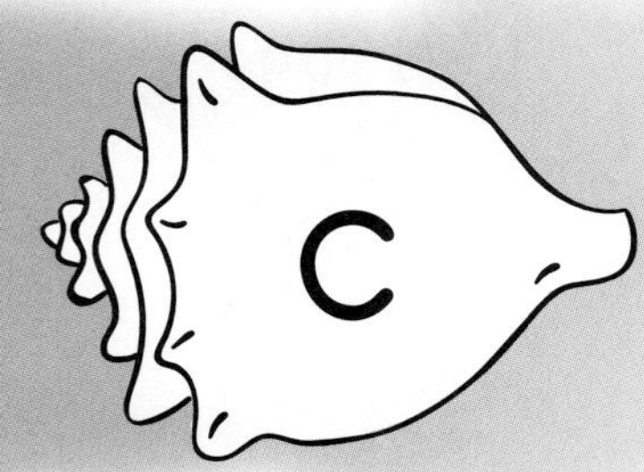

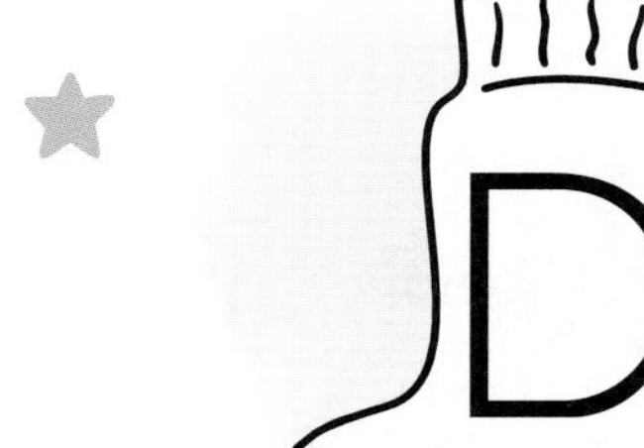

Color the uppercase and lowercase form of the same letter.

Name ______________________________

Look at the picture. Which car won the race? Circle that car.
Which car had a flat tire? Draw a line under that car.
Which car was the rabbit driving? Draw an X on that car.

Ee Ff

Name ____________________

Name the letters in each box. • Color the pictures that show the uppercase and lowercase forms of the same letter.

Name________________________________ the

the

the

the

the

Say the word and picture. Draw a circle around the word *the*. Draw your own toy after the word *the*. Then draw a circle around the word *the*.

Gg 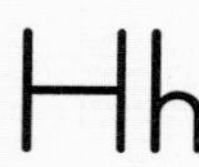

Name____________________

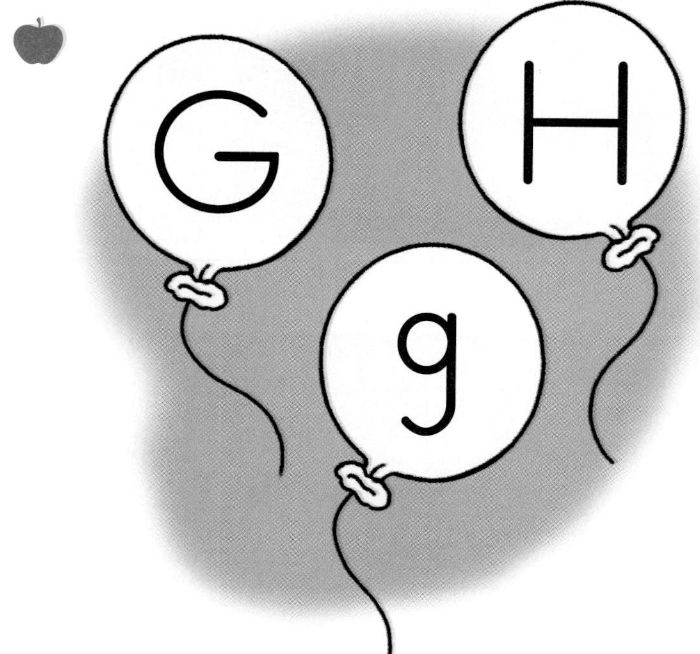

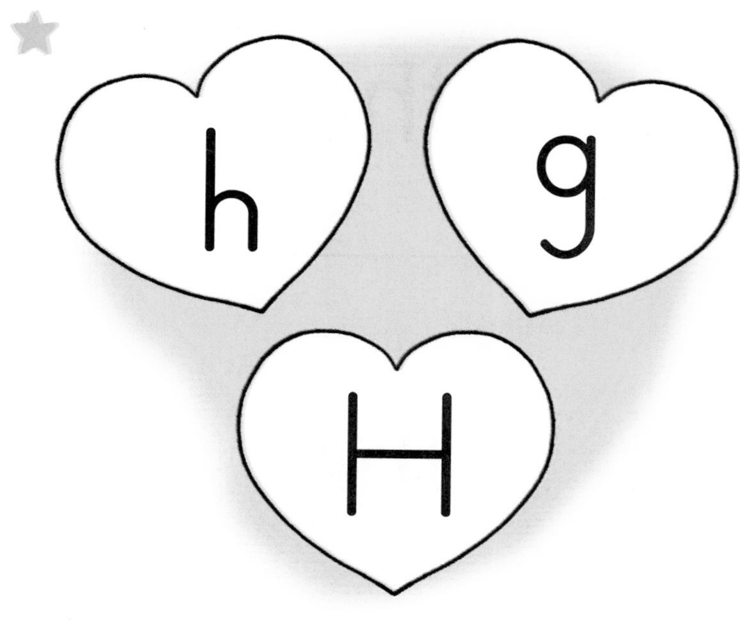

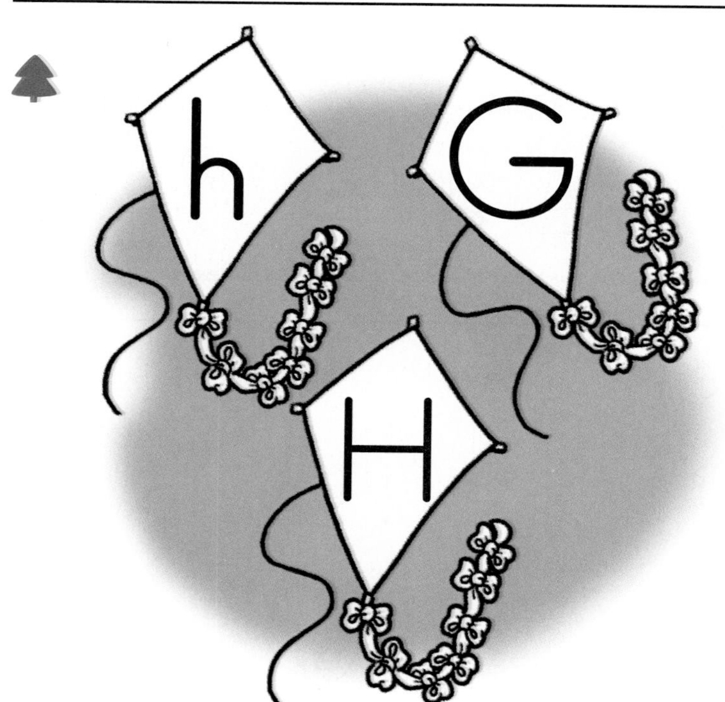

Name the letters in each box. • Color the pictures that show the uppercase and lowercase forms of the same letter.

the

The 

the 

the 

the

the 

the 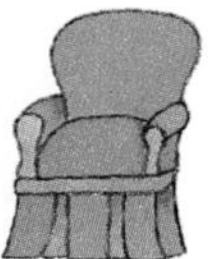

McGraw-Hill School Division

the 

Name ______________________________

Look at the picture of clothes on the clothesline. What item of clothing has flowers on it? Circle it. What has buttons? Underline it. What can someone wear to go swimming? Put an X on it.

Ii Jj Kk

Name________________________

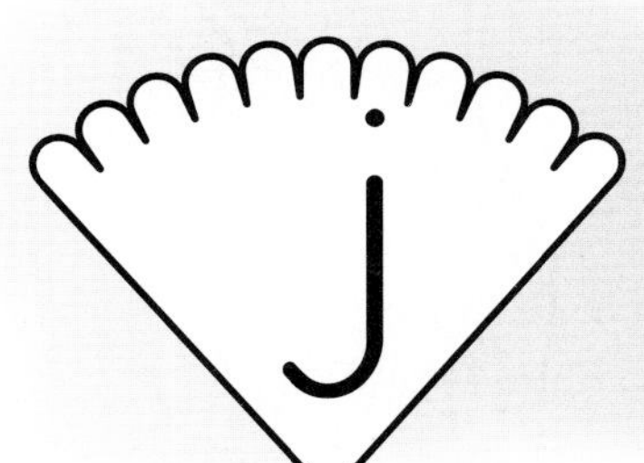

K

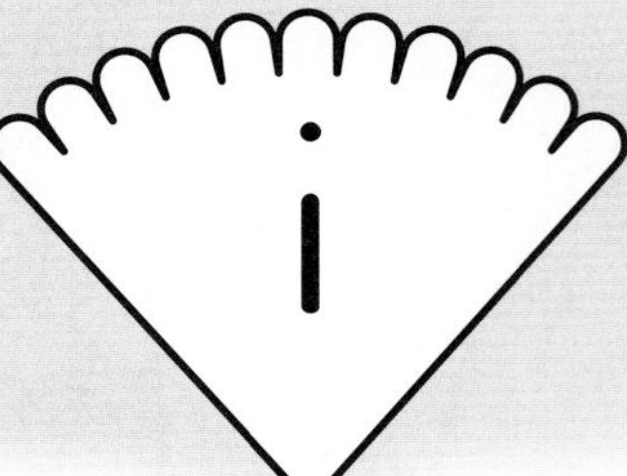

k

i

Color the uppercase and lowercase form of the same letter.

Name____

the

the

the

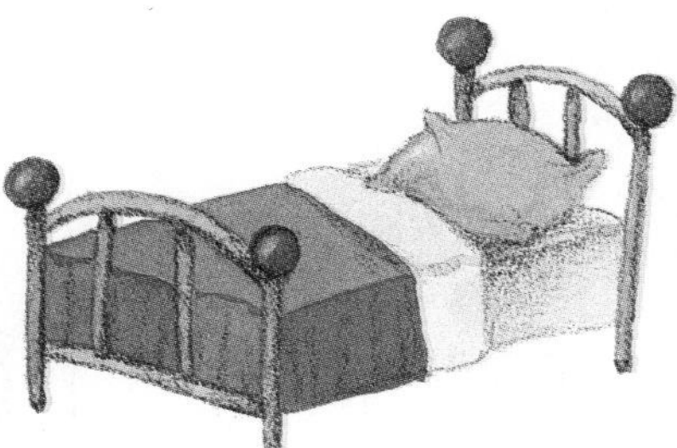

the

the

Say the word and picture. Draw a circle around the word *the*. Draw a picture of something in your house. Then draw a circle around the word *the*.

Ll Mm Nn

Name ____________________

Color the uppercase and lowercase form of the same letter.

Name

Draw a circle around the first item in each row. • Draw a line under the next item in each row. • Cross out the last item in each row.

Oo Pp Qq

Name________________________________

Q q
p

Name the letters in each box. • Color the pictures that show the uppercase and lowercase forms of the same letter.

Name ____________________

Talk about what is happening in the first box. Circle what happens next. Draw a box around what happens last. • Repeat for the second row.

Rr Ss Tt

Name________________________________

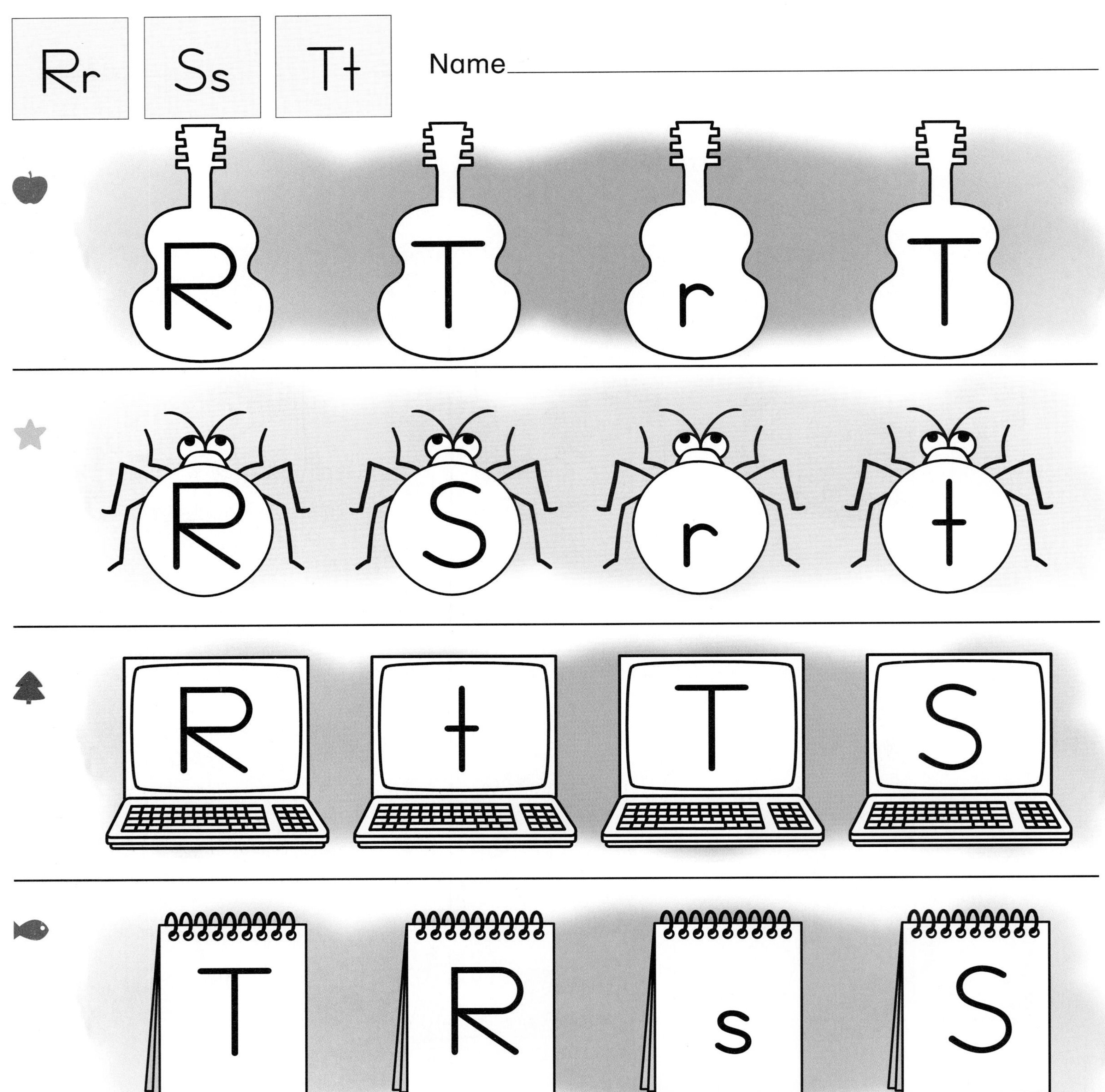

Color the uppercase and lowercase form of the same letter.

Name ______________________

a

a

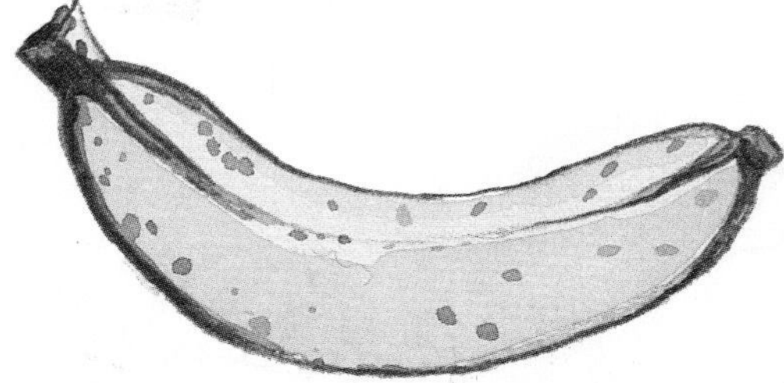

a

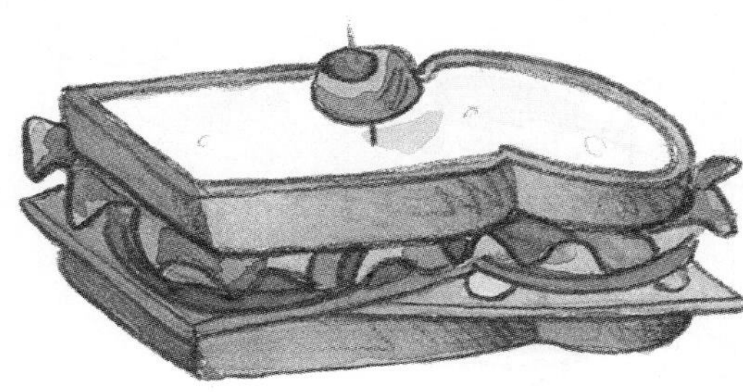

a

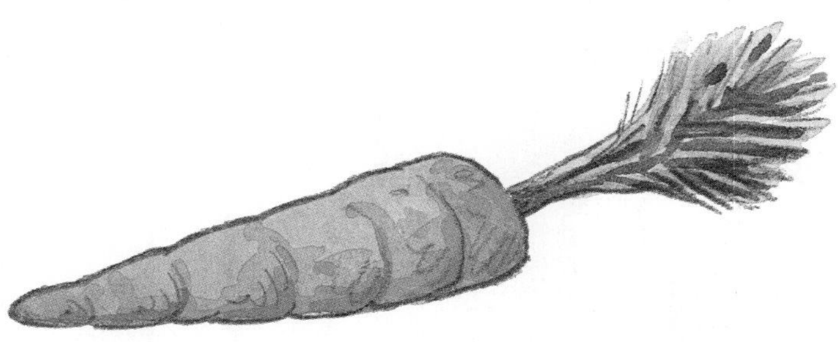

a

Say the word and picture. Draw a circle around the word *a.* Draw a picture of something you might eat after the word *a.* You can choose to draw a hamburger, a peach, a muffin, or a plum. Then draw a circle around the word *a.*

Uu

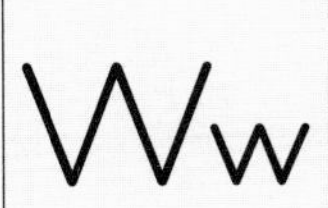

Ww

Name________________________________

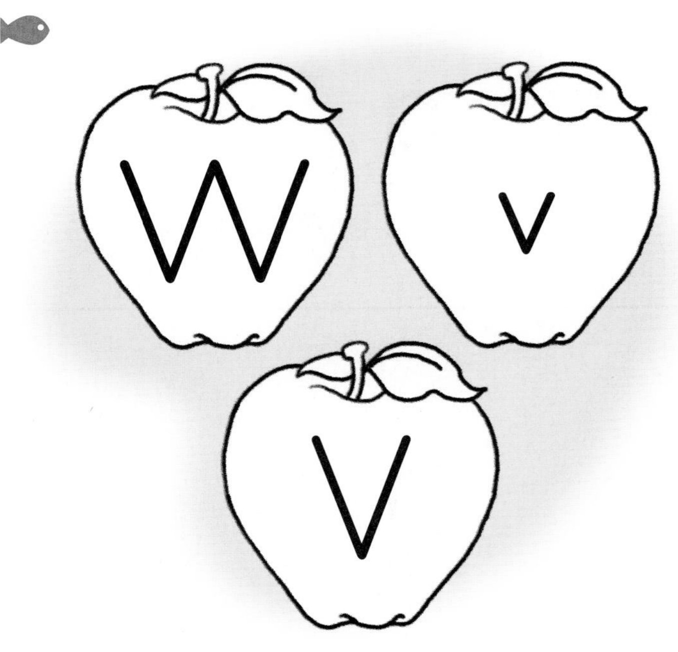

Name the letters in each box. • Color the pictures that show the uppercase and lowercase forms of the same letter.

a

A 

a

a 

a 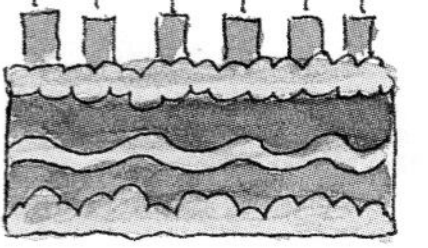

a 

a 

a 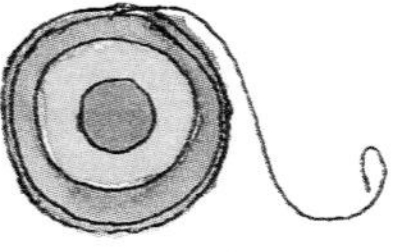

Name____

Talk about what is happening in the first box. Circle what happens next. Draw a box around what happens last. Repeat for the second row.

Xx Yy Zz Name

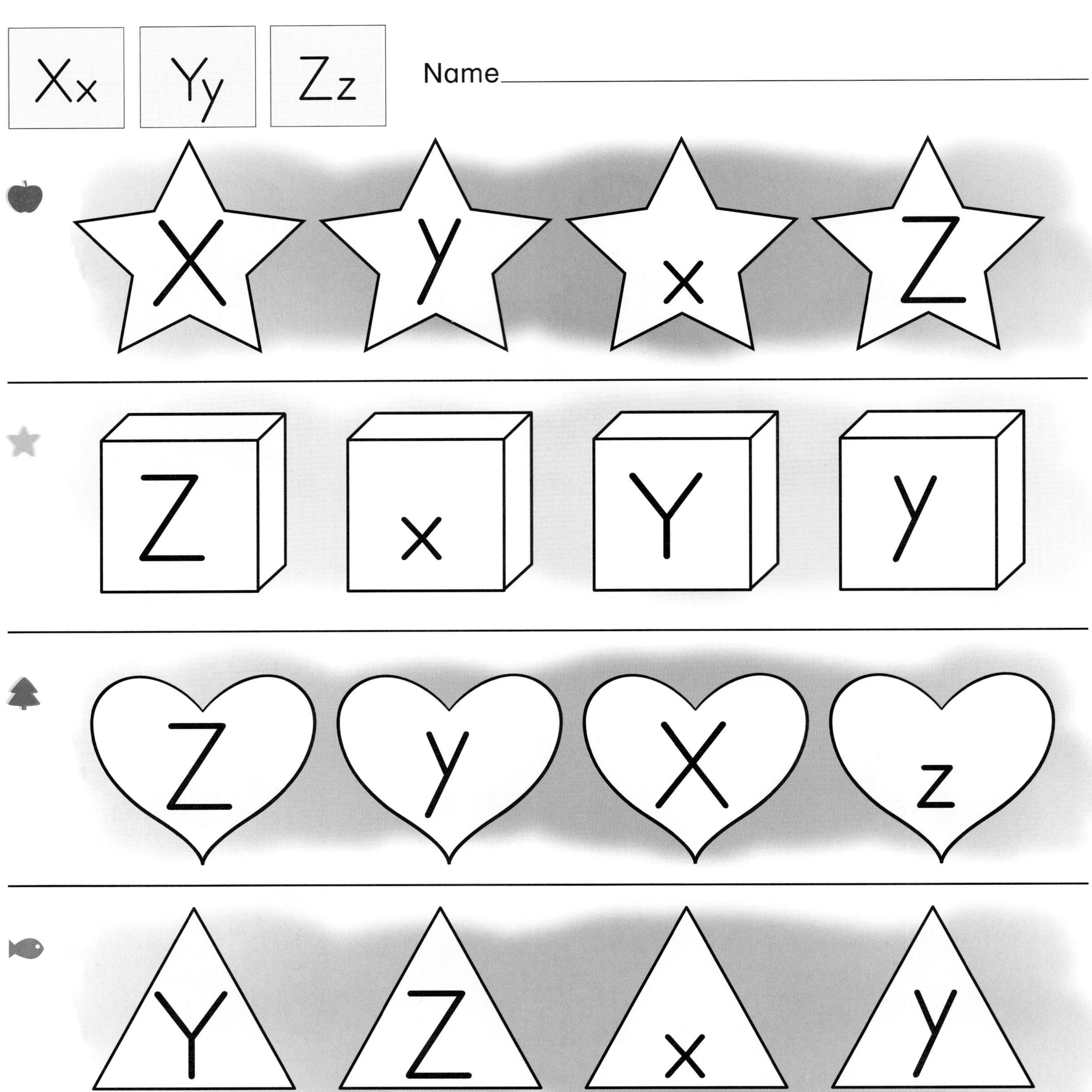

Color the uppercase and lowercase form of the same letter.

Name

a

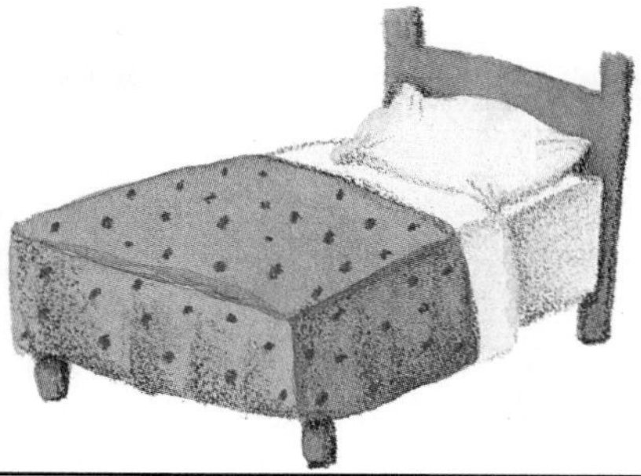

a

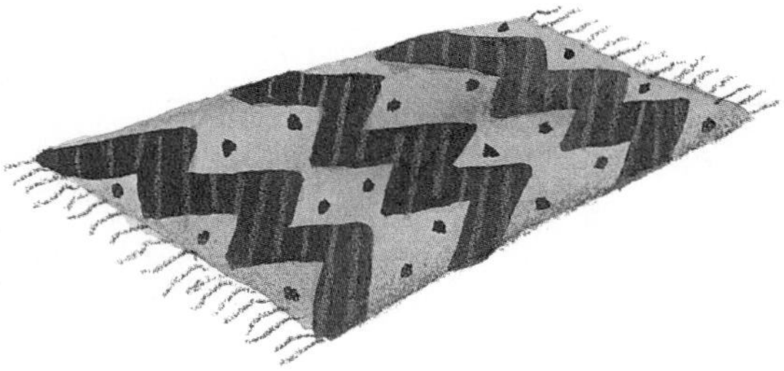

the

the

Say the word and picture. Draw a circle around the word *a*. Say the word and picture. Draw a line under the word *the*.

Name_______________________________

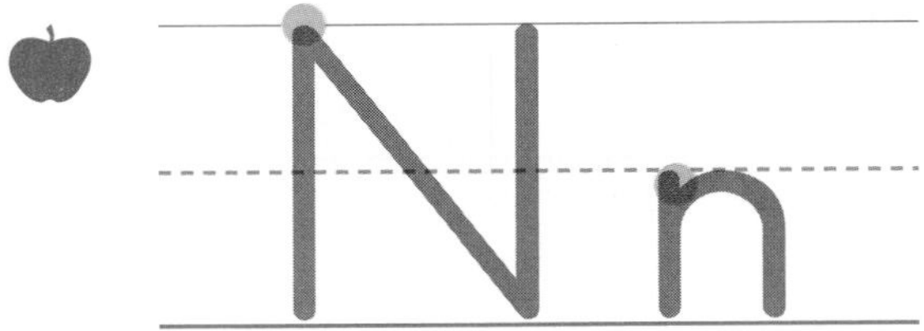

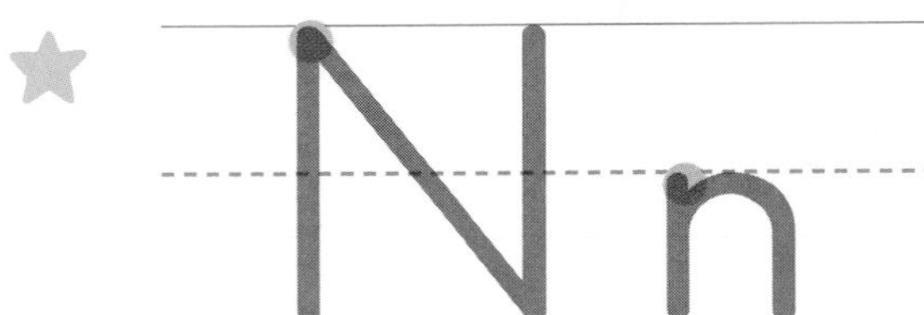

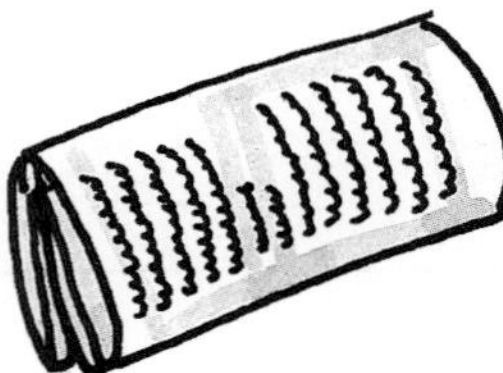

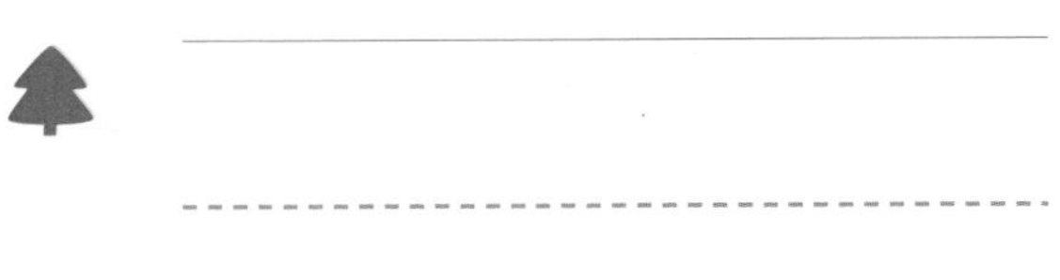

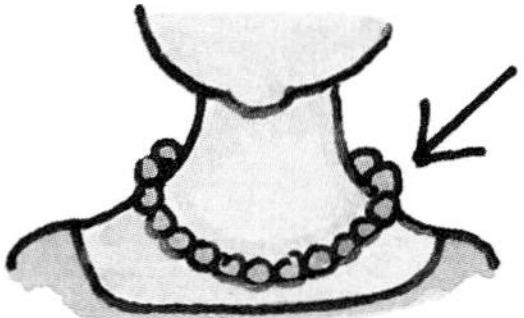

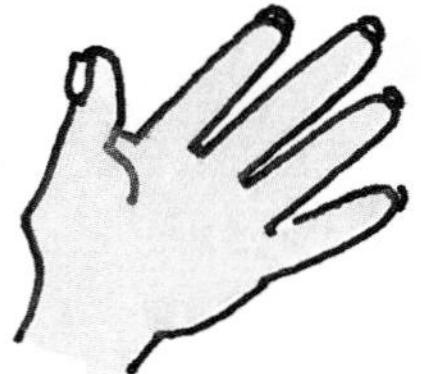

Write the letters *Nn.* • Say the word that names each picture. • Listen for the sound at the beginning of each word. • Circle each picture whose name begins with the same sound as *nail.*

Name

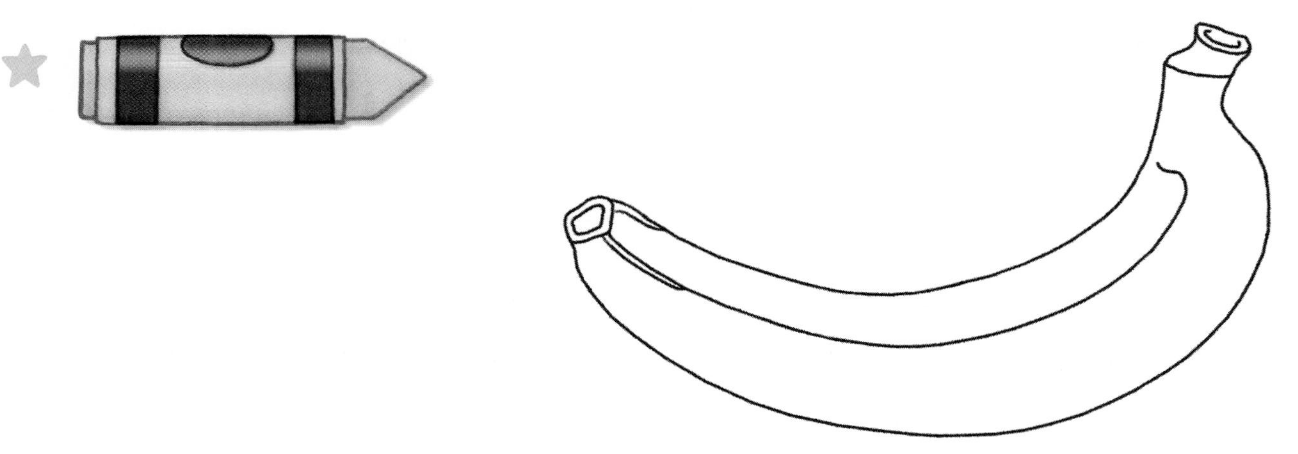

Color each item to match the color of the crayon.

___n

Name ______________________________

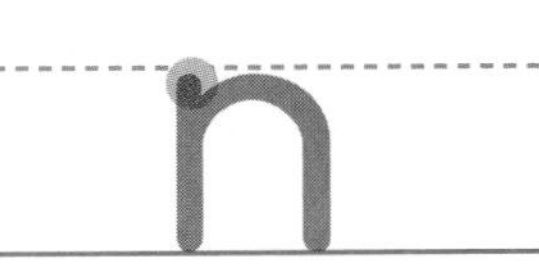

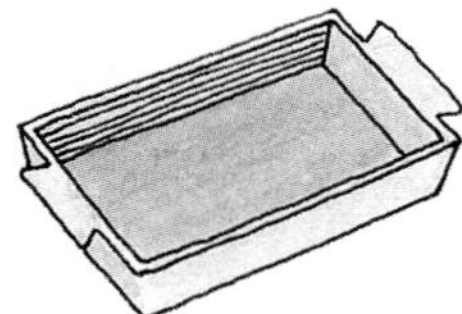

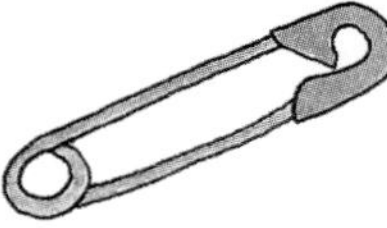

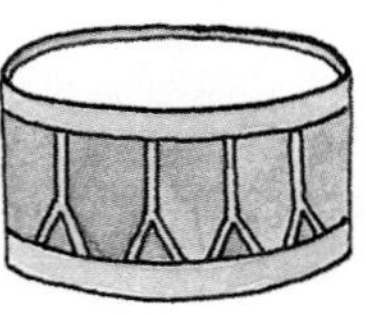

Say the name of each picture. • Circle the pictures whose names have the same ending sound as *sun.* • Write the letter *n.*

Name______________________________________

Look at the picture. Did the teacher bring something to share? Color it green. Did someone bring a doll? Color the doll yellow. Use a red crayon to color the toy with wheels.

Name ____________________

n

n

n

n

n

Trace the letter. Say the name of each picture. Then write the letter in the correct box to show if you hear the sound /n/ at the beginning, the middle, or the end of the word.

Name ______________________

my

my

my

my

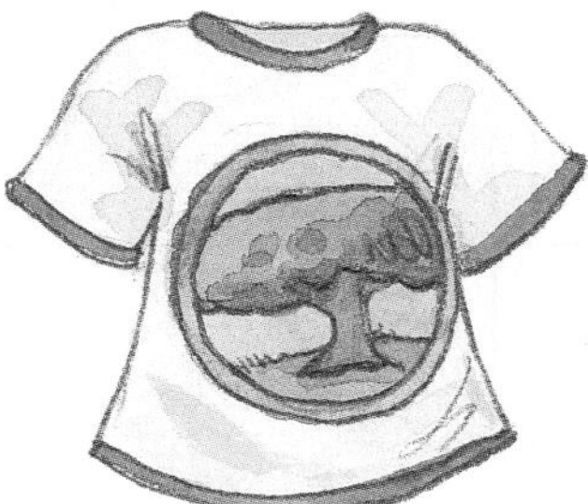

my

Say the word and picture. Draw a circle around the word *my*. Draw a picture of something you wear after the word *my*. Then draw a circle around the word *my*.

Name____

R	R	B	R	P
M	V	M	N	M
S	S	R	Z	S
n	m	n	r	n
p	p	q	p	g

Look at the first letter in each row. • Circle the same letter each time you see it in the row.

my 

8

My 

my 

6

my 

3

my

my

my

my

Name____

Look at the picture. What is in the wheelbarrow? Circle it.
What are the rabbits eating? Underline it.
Which animals are flying? Draw an X on them.

Name ____

I	J	I	L	I
O	O	Q	C	O
Y	V	Y	K	Y
l	l	i	t	l
v	w	v	u	v

Look at the first letter in each row. • Circle the same letter each time you see it in the row.

Name ______________________________

my

my

a

the

Say the word and picture. • Draw a circle around the word in front of the picture.

Name ____________________

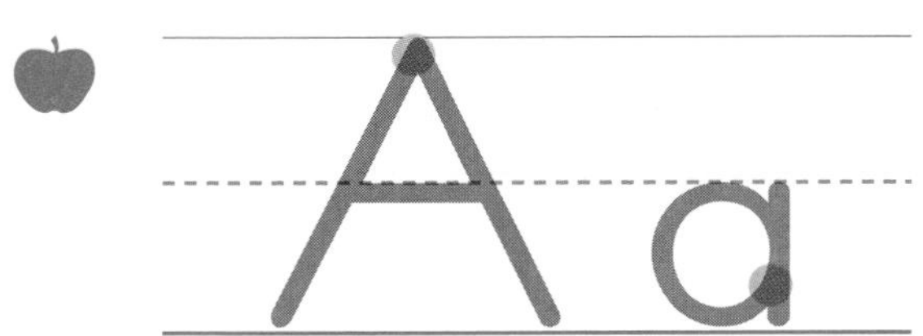

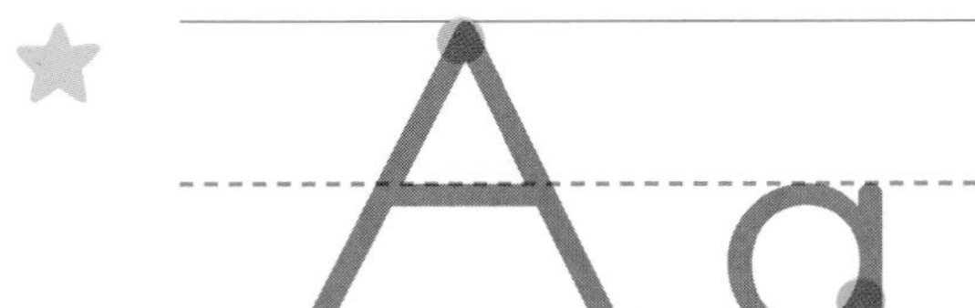
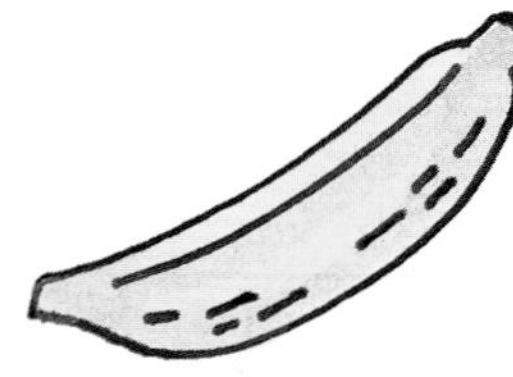

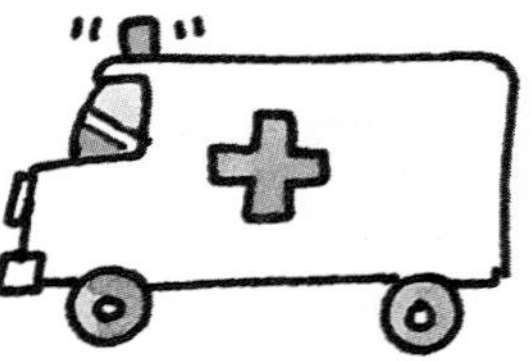

Write the letters *Aa*. Say the word that names each picture. Circle each picture whose name begins with the same sound as *apple*.

Name ____________________

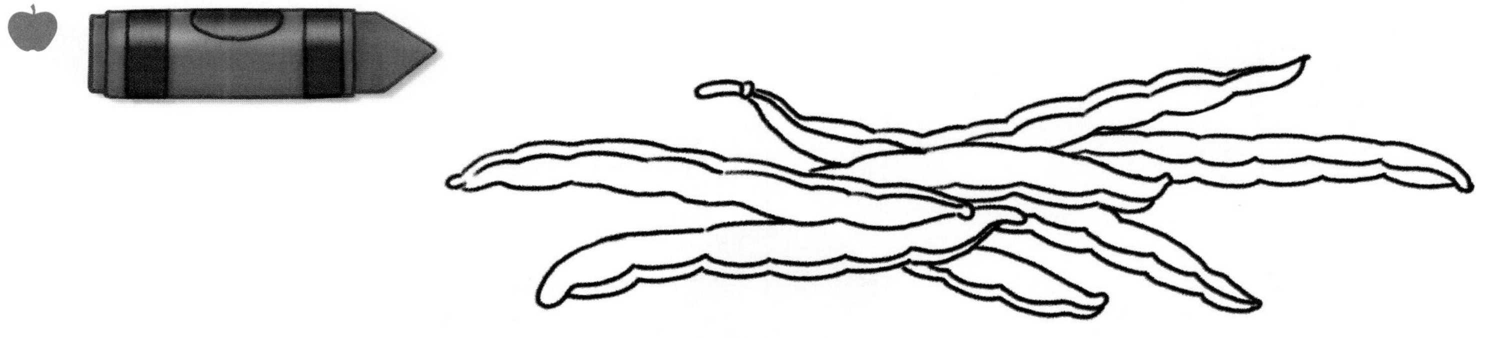

Color each item to match the color of the crayon.

Name ______________________

McGraw-Hill School Division

Write the letter *a*. • Say the word that names each picture. • Listen for the sound in the middle of each word. • Circle each picture whose name has the same middle sound as *cat*.

Name____

Talk about what is happening in the first box. Circle what happens next.
Draw a box around what happens last. Repeat for the second row.

Name ___

a

a

a

a

a

Trace the letter. Say the word that names the picture. Then write the letter in the correct box to show if you hear the sound /a/ at the beginning, the middle, or the end of the word.

Name ______________________

that

that

that

that

that

Say the word and picture. Draw a circle around the word *that*. Draw a picture of a car after the word *that*. Then draw a circle around the word *that*.

Name________________________________

Say each letter sound at the top of the page. On the apple and star rows blend the sounds and say the words. Write the words. Use each word in a sentence.

That Nan!

Nan

Nan

Nan

Nan

Nan

Nan

Nan

Name ______________________________

Talk about what happens in the first box. Circle what happens next.
Draw a box around what happens last. • Repeat for the second row.

Name

a n

a n

N a n

Blend the sounds and write the word. Read the word and the picture name.

Name________________________________

that

a

the

my

Say the word and picture. • Draw a circle around the word in front of the picture.

Name ______________________________

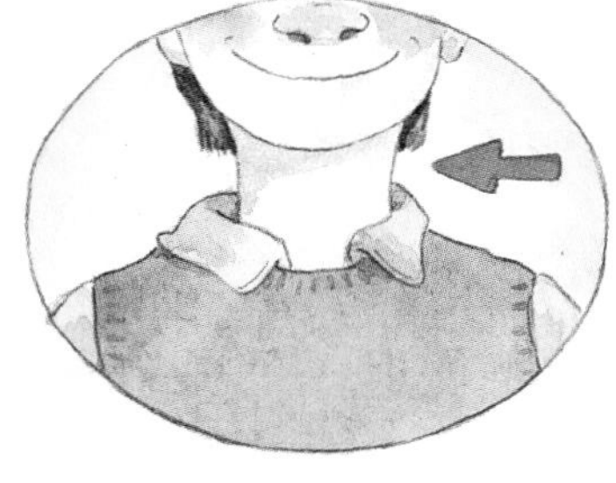

Say the name of each picture. • Under the picture write the letter for the sound you hear at the beginning of the picture name.

Name ______________________________

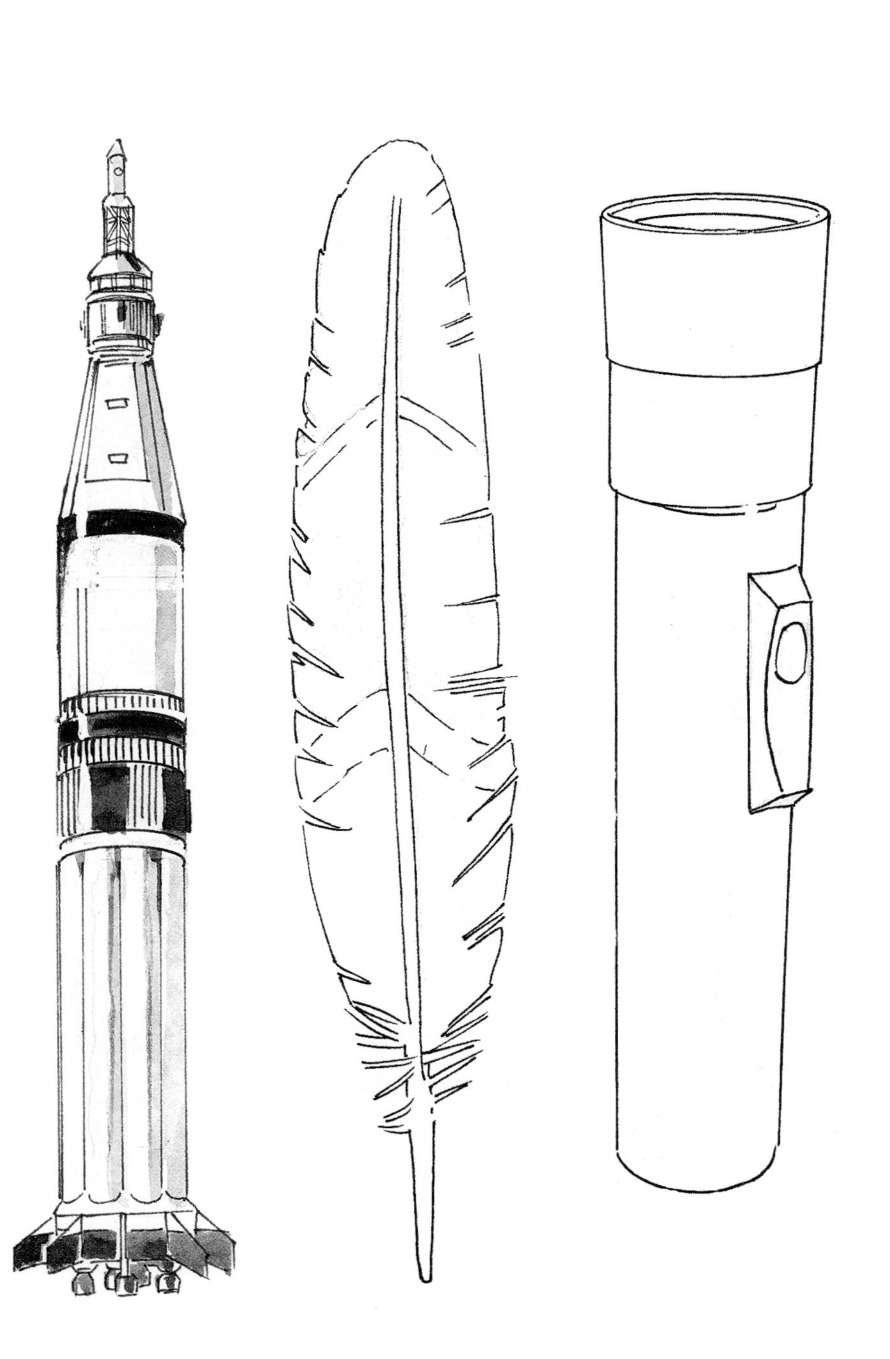

On the left part of the page, color the first item red. • Color the next item blue. • Color the last item green. • On the right part of the page, draw something you could bring to a show-and-tell day at school.

Name

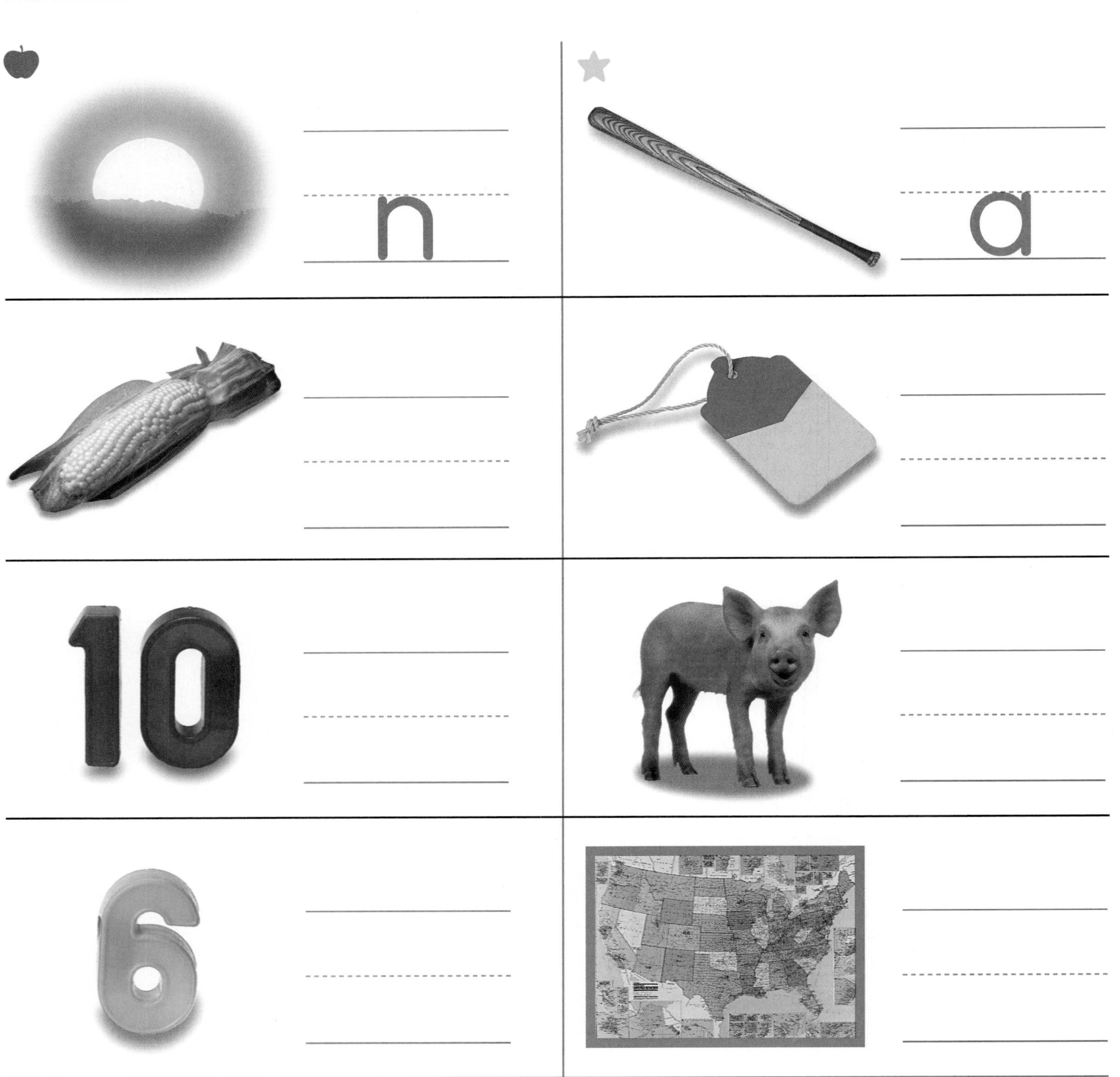

Say the word that names each picture. Write the letter n on the line if you hear the /n/*n* sound at the end of the word. Write the letter a on the line if you hear the /a/*a* sound in the middle of the word.

Name ____________________

Use a red crayon to color what the girl made. Use a blue crayon to color what the boy made. Use a green crayon to color what the teacher made.

Name

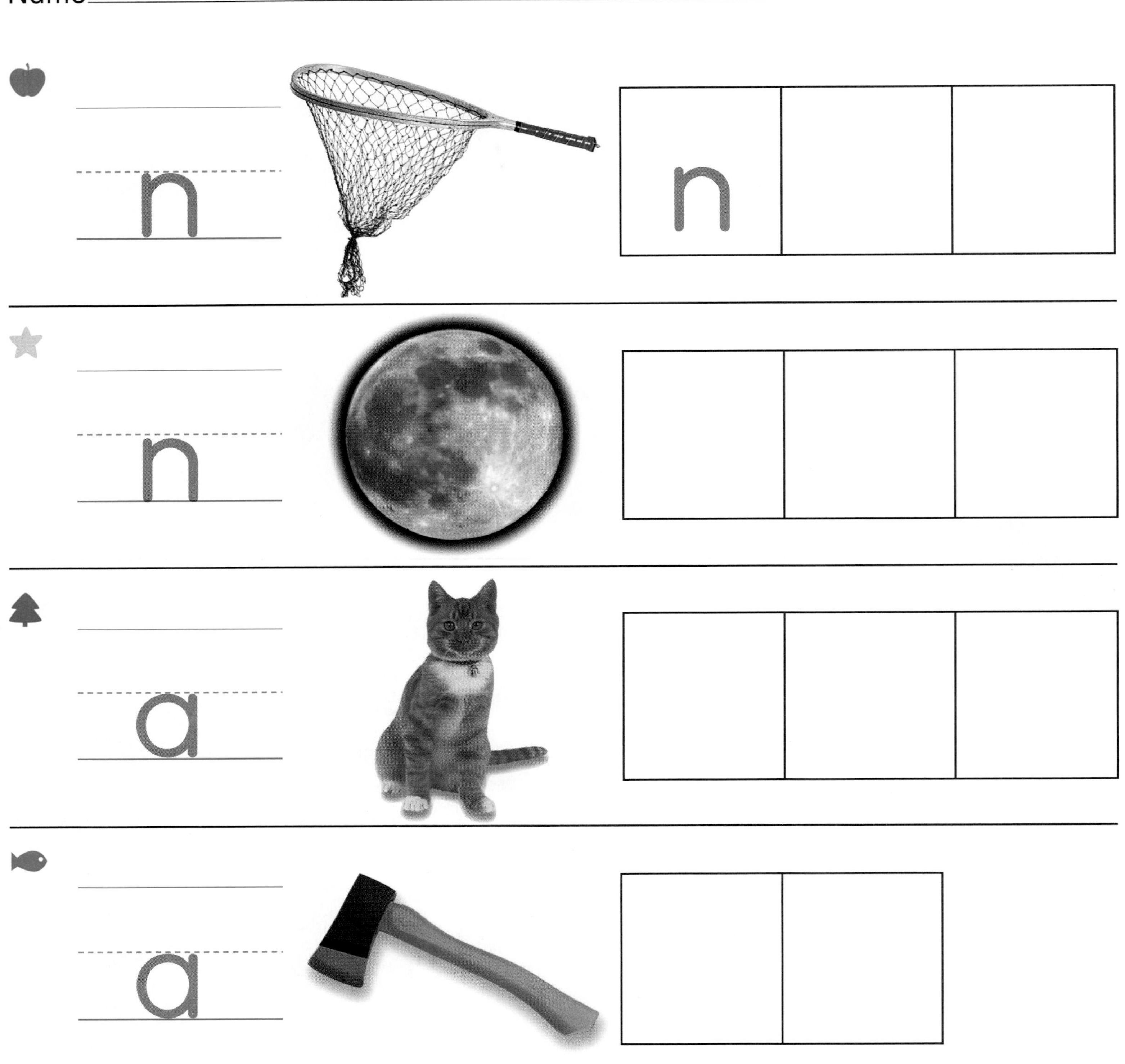

Trace the letter. Say the name of each picture. Write the letter in the correct box to show if you hear the sound /a/ or /n/ at the beginning, the middle, or the end of the word.

Name______________________________

a	the	a	that
my	a	that	my
the	a	the	my
that	the	that	my

Say the first word in the row. • Draw a circle around the word where you see it in the same row.

Name

a n

an

a n

a n

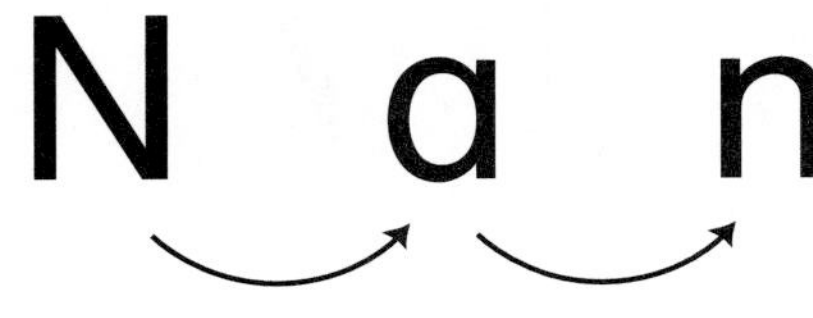

N a n

Blend the sounds and write the word. Read the word and picture name aloud.
Blend the sounds and write the name. Read the sentence that is made up of the word and picture name.

That Nan!

That Nan!

Nan?

Nan

Nan

Nan?

McGraw-Hill School Division

Nan

Nan

Name ________________________________

Draw a circle around the picture that shows what happened first. • Draw a line under the picture that shows what happened next. • Draw a box around the picture that shows what happened last.

Name

a n

a n

a n

N a n

Blend the sounds and write the word. Read the word and the picture name. Blend the sounds and write the name. Read the sentence that is made up of the word and the name of the picture.

Name ______________________________

a	that	the	my
my	the	a	that
that	a	the	my
the	my	that	a

Read the four words in each row. Draw a circle around the word *the*. Draw a circle around the word *a*. Draw a circle around the word *my*. Draw a circle around the word *that*.

Name________________________________

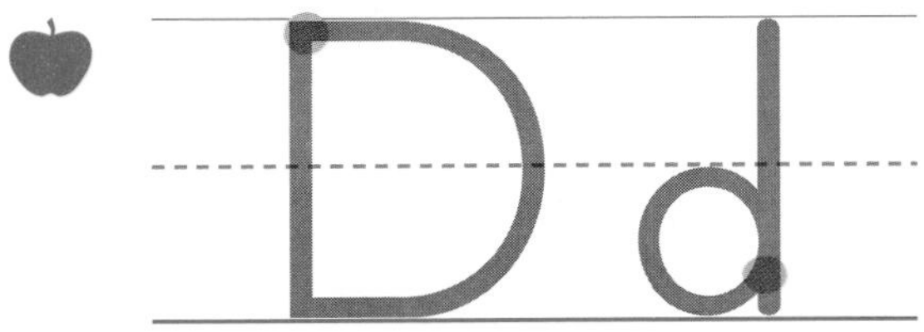

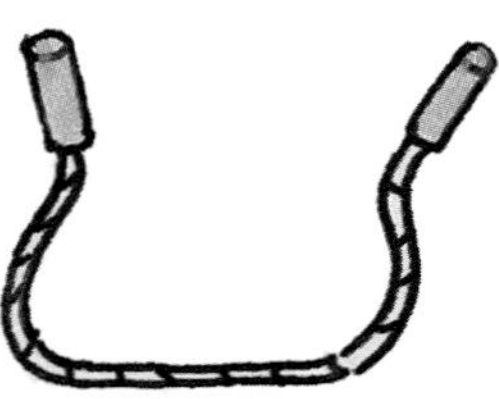

Write the letters *Dd*. • Say the word that names each picture. • Listen for the sound at the beginning of each word. • Draw a circle around each picture whose name begins with the same sound as *dog*.

Name ____________________

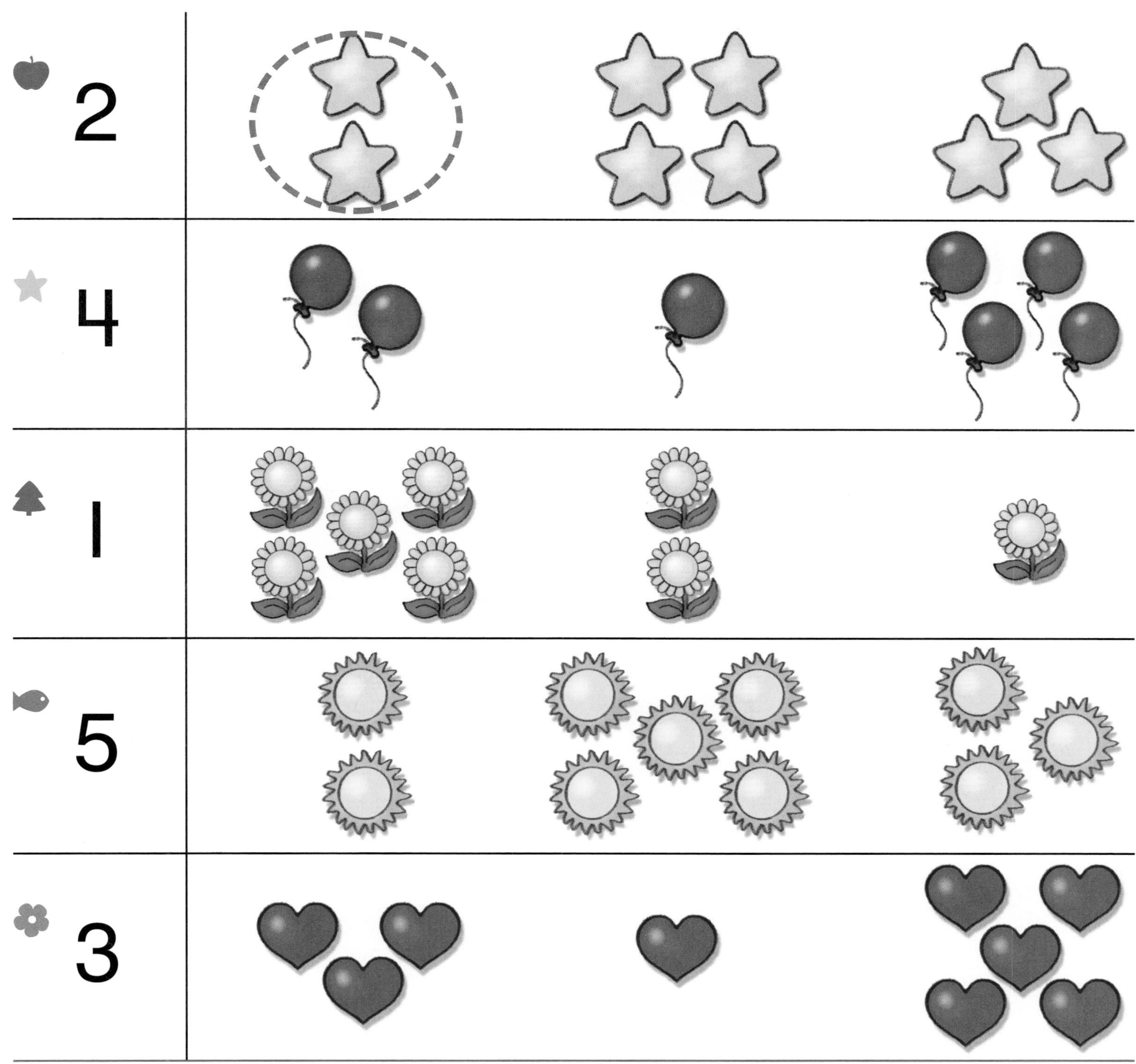

Draw a circle around the group of objects in each row that shows the number on the left.

_d

Name ____________________

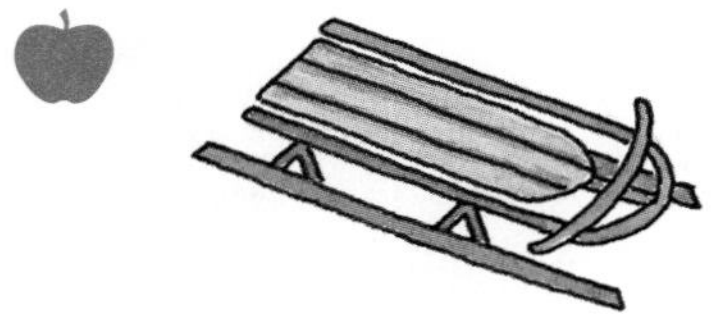

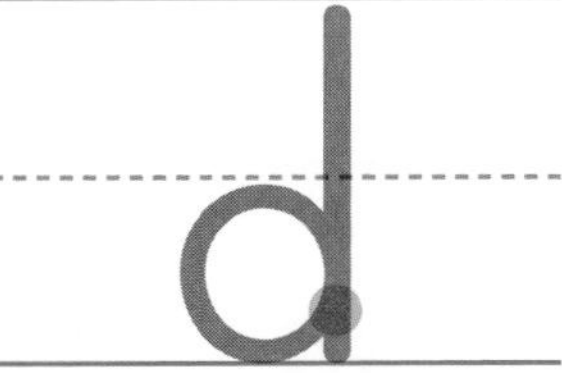

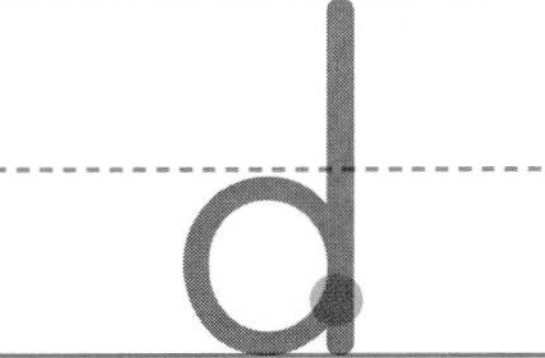

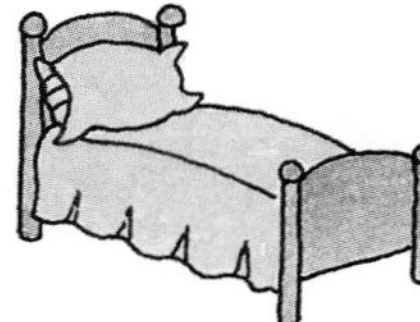
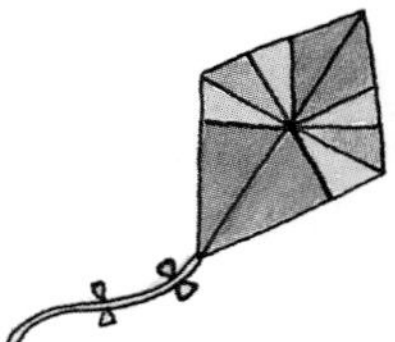

Say the name of each picture. • Circle each picture that has the same ending sound as *bed*. • Write the letter *d*.

Name ______________________________

Think about the story "Warthogs in the Kitchen." 🍎 Circle the picture that shows a place in the story. ★ Circle the picture that shows a character from the story. 🌲 Circle the picture that shows something else from the story.

Name ____________________

d

d		

d

d

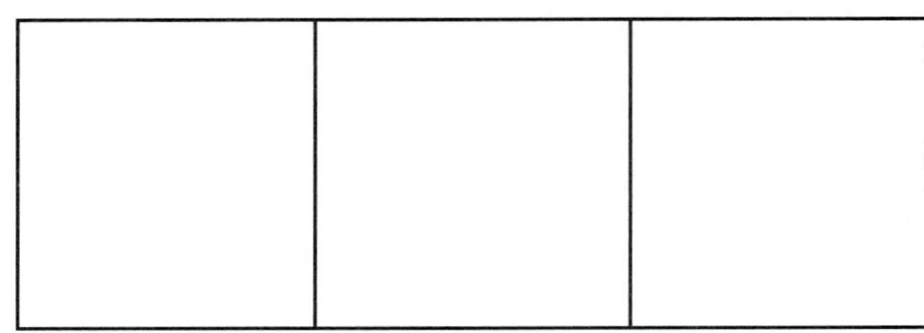

d

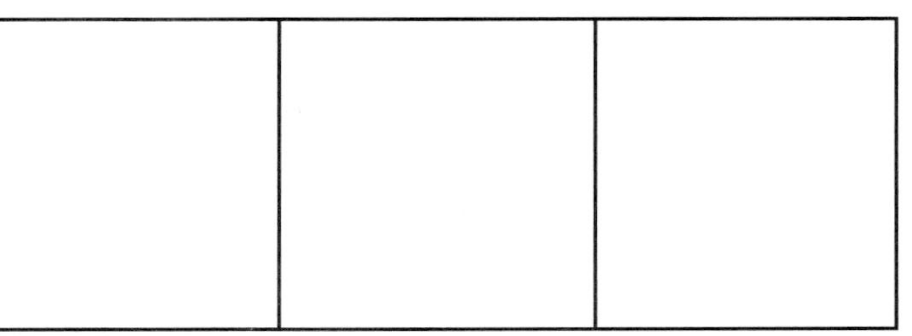

Trace the letter. Say the word that names each picture. Write the letter in the correct box to show if you hear the sound /d/ at the beginning, middle, or the end of the word.

Name ______________________________

and

Nan and Dan

Dan and Dad

Dad and Nan

Read the words in each row. • Draw a line under the word *and*.

Name ____________________

N a n

Nan

D a n

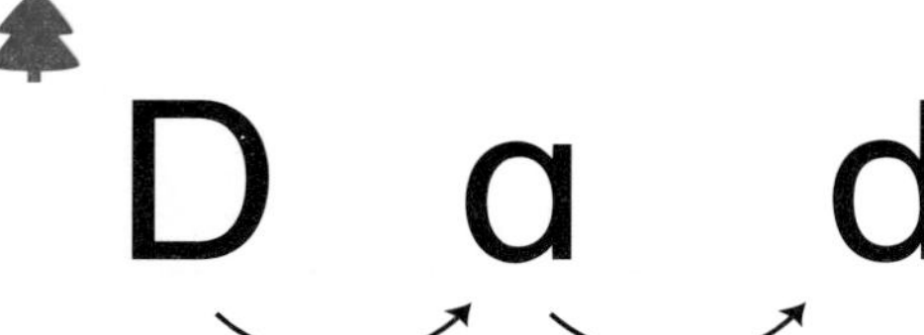

D a d

a n

Blend the sounds and write the name. Say the name of the picture.

Blend the sounds and write the word. Say the word and the name of the picture.

Dan and my Nan

Dan and Dad

my Nan

Dan

Nan

Dan and my dad

Dad

my dad

Name ____

Think about the story "Dan and Dad." Circle the picture that shows a place in the story. Circle the picture that shows characters from the story. Circle the picture that shows a character and a place in the story.

Name ______________________________

Dad Nan

Nan Dan

Nan Dan

Dan Dad

Look at each picture. • Read the names. Draw a circle around the name that goes with the picture. • Write the name.

Name ____________________

Dan and a 

Nan and my Dad

Dan and

Read the words. Draw a circle around the word *and*. Draw a line under the word *a*. Draw two lines under the word *my*. Draw a picture of a friend. Then read the words in this row again with the name of the person in the picture.

Name

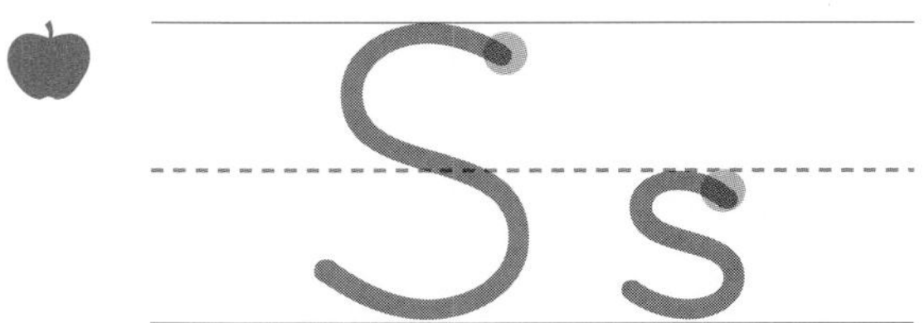

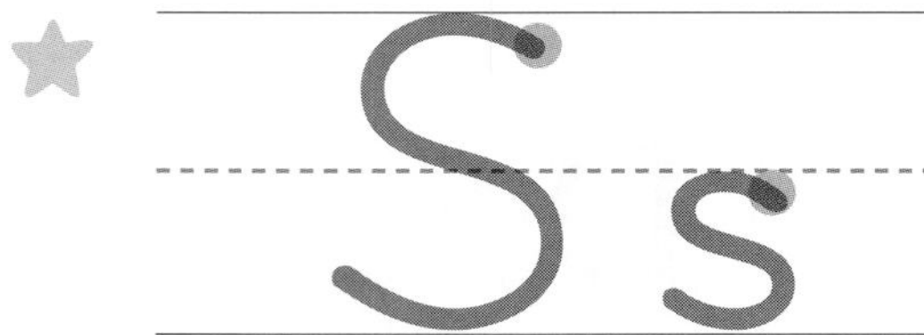

Write the letters *Ss*. • Say the word that names each picture. • Listen for the sound at the beginning of each word. • Draw a circle around each picture whose name begins with the same sound as *soap*.

Name ______________________________

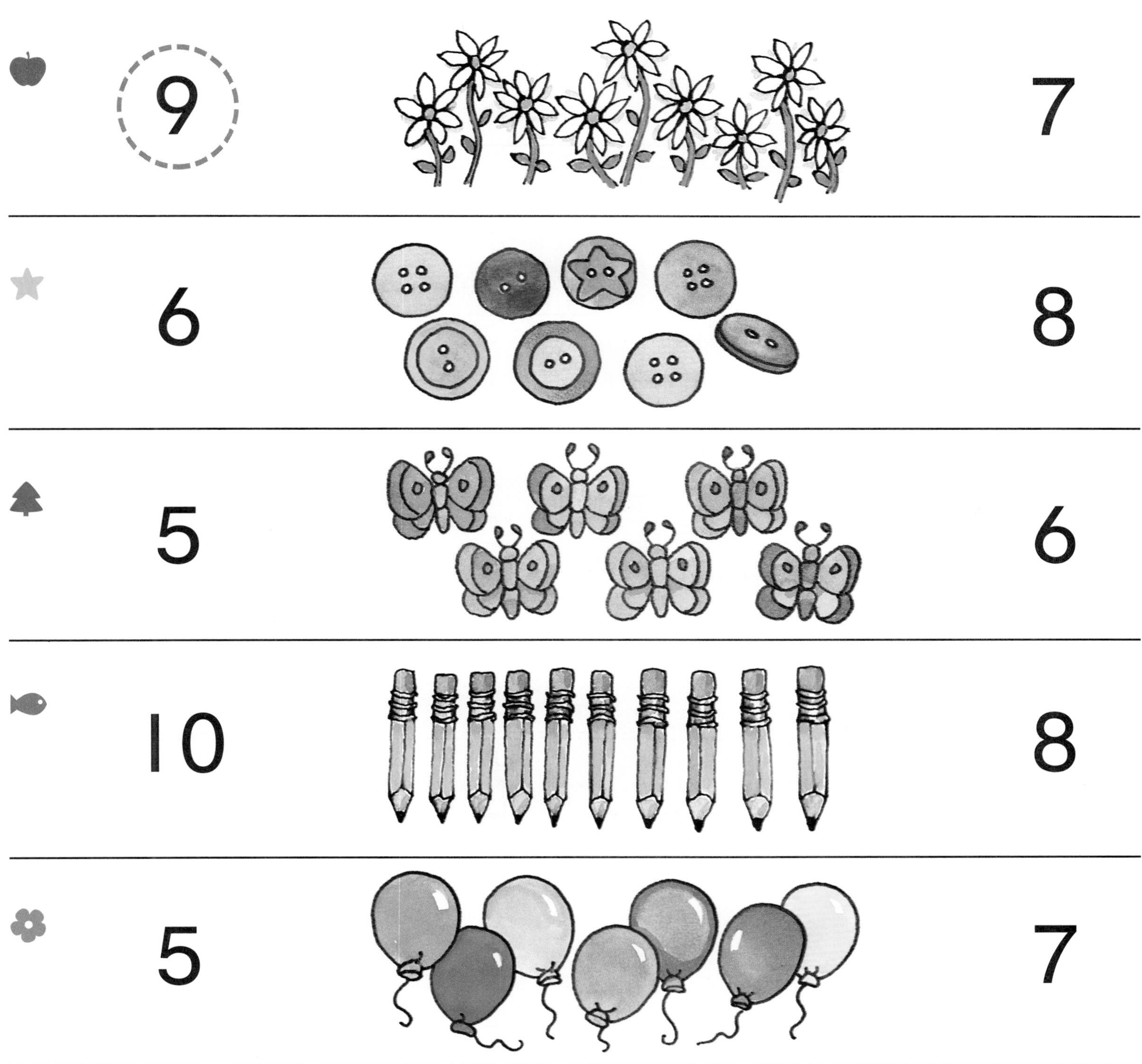

Draw a circle around the number that shows how many objects are in each row.

Name ____________________

Ss

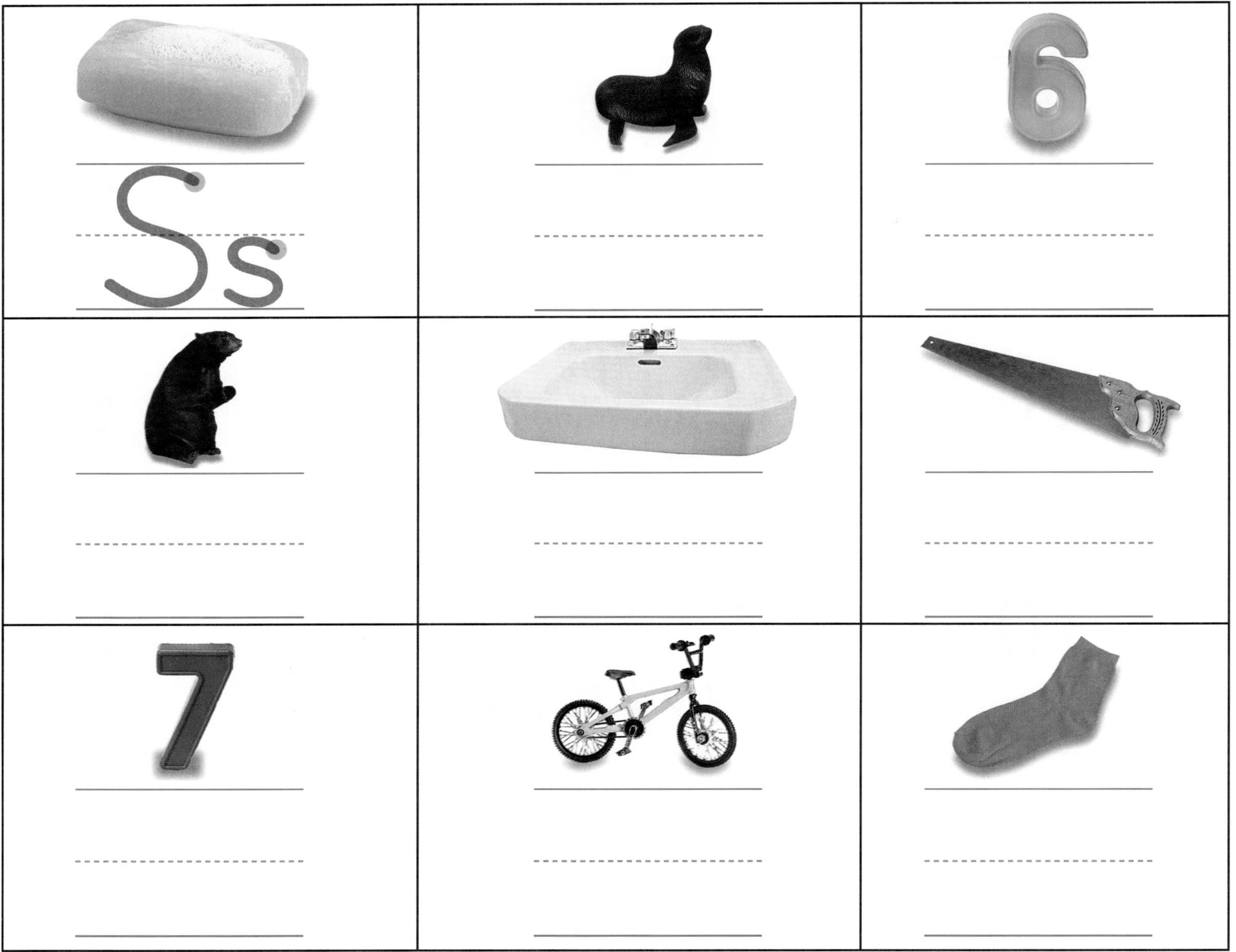

Say the word that names the picture. If the word begins with the /s/ sound, write the letters *Ss* on the line.

Name____

Draw a circle around the picture that does not belong.

Name

Trace the letter. Say the word that names each picture. Write the letter in the correct box to show if you hear the sound /s/ or /d/ at the beginning, the middle, or the end of the word.

McGraw-Hill School Division

Name________________________________

I

I

I

I

I

Say the word and picture. Draw a circle around the word *I*. Draw a picture of yourself doing something you like to do after the word *I*. Then draw a circle around the word *I*.

Name ____________________

s a d

sad

D a d

D a n

N a n

Blend the sounds and say the word. Write the word. Draw a circle around the picture that goes with the word.

Sad and and !

Dad, Dan, and I

sad

Dan and I

Dad, Dan, and I

sad and 

Dad and Dan

Dad and I

Name ______________________________

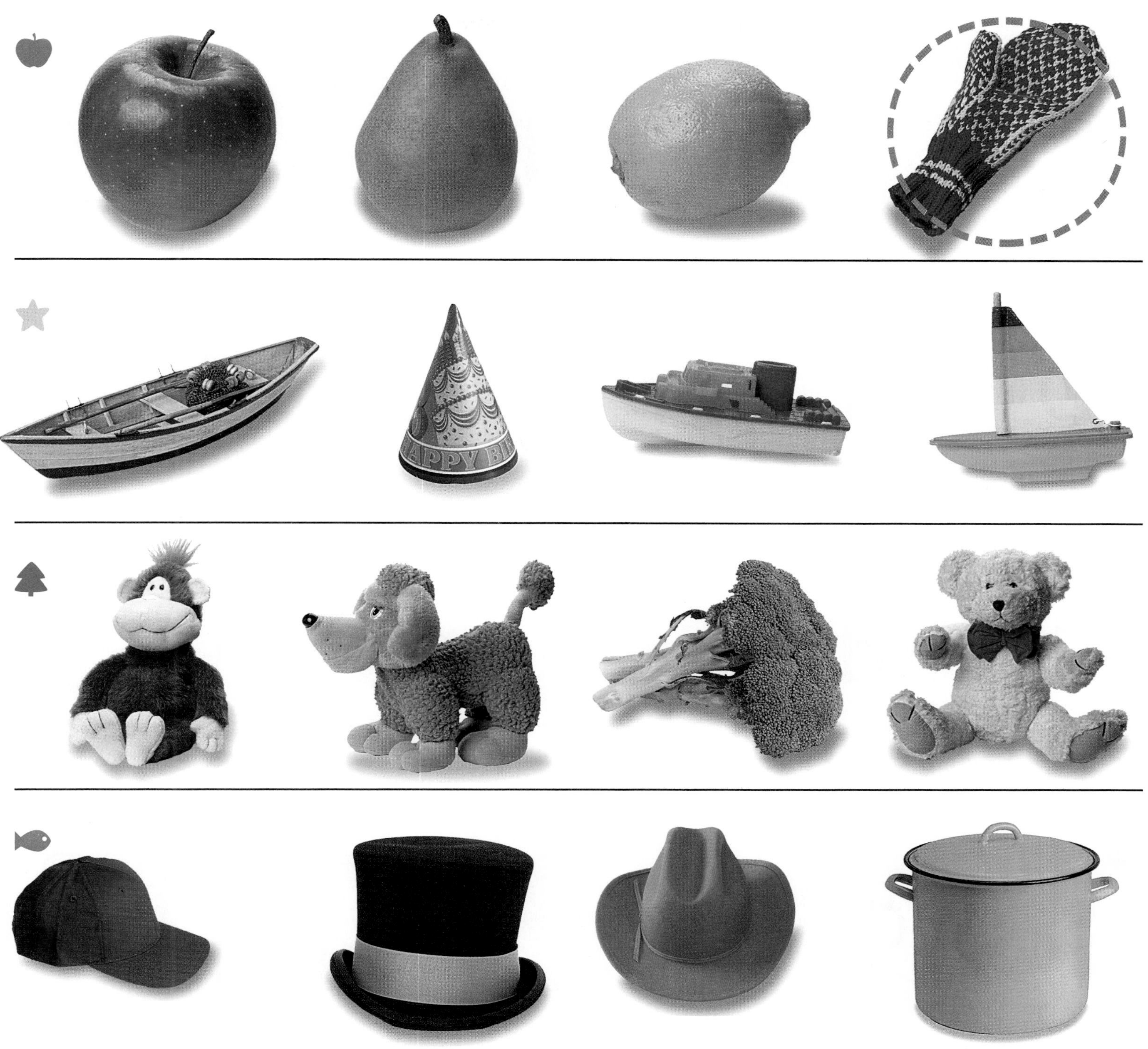

Look at the pictures in each row. • Draw a circle around the picture that does not belong.

Name ______________________________

N a n

Nan

D a n

D a d

s a d

McGraw-Hill School Division

Blend the sounds and write the word. Say the word that names each picture.

Name ____________________

Nan and I

My dad and Nan

My dad and I

I

Say each group of words and the picture names. Draw a circle around the word *I*. Draw a circle around the word *and* . Draw a circle around the word *my*. Next to the word *I* draw a picture yourself doing something. Then draw a circle around the word *I*.

Name______________________________

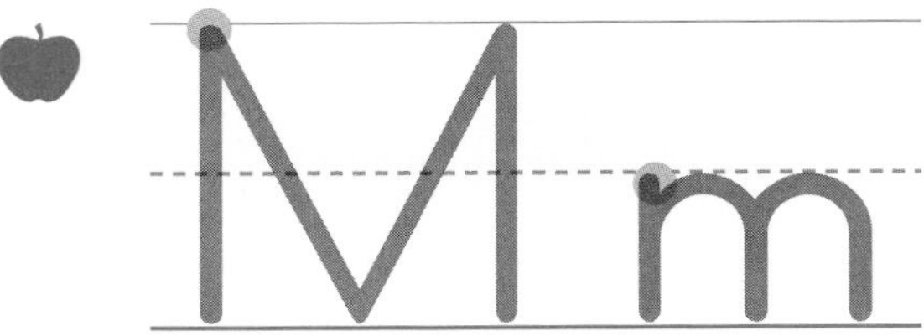

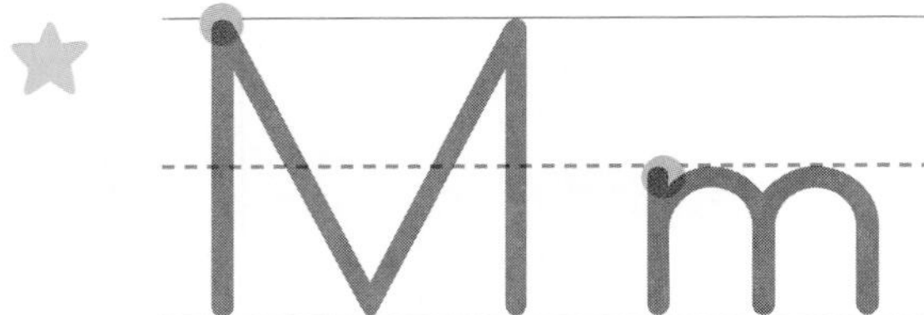

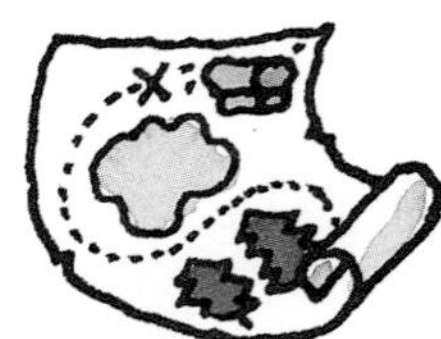

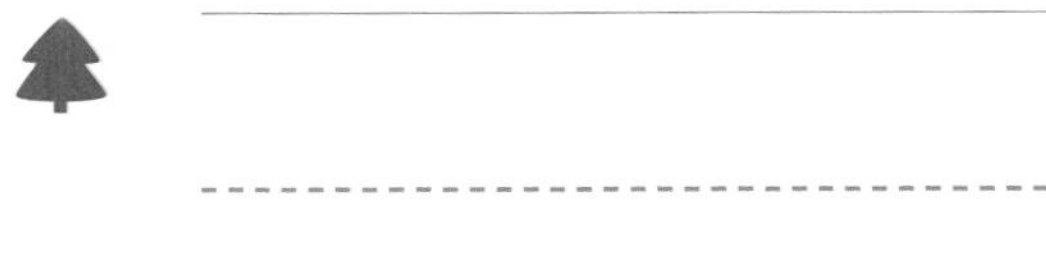

Write the letters *Mm.* • Say the word that names each picture. • Listen for the sound at the beginning of each word. • Draw a circle around each picture whose name begins with the same sound as *mitt.*

Name______________________________

Color the shapes that are the same in each row.

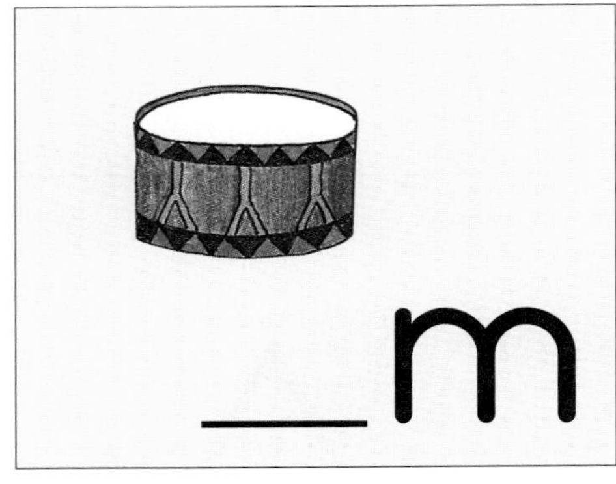

Name________________________________

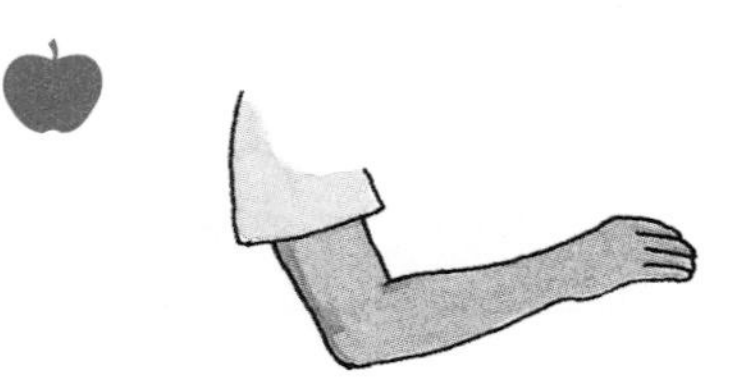

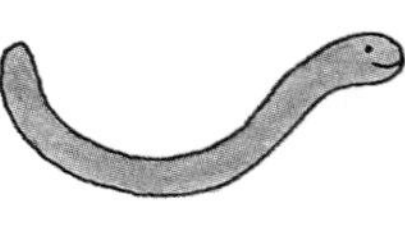

Say the name of each picture. • Circle the pictures whose names have the same ending sound as *drum.* • Write the letter *m.*

Name ____________________

Think about the story "Chick and the Duckling." Circle the picture that shows a character from the story. Circle the picture that shows another character from the story. Circle the picture that shows a place in the story.

Name ____________________

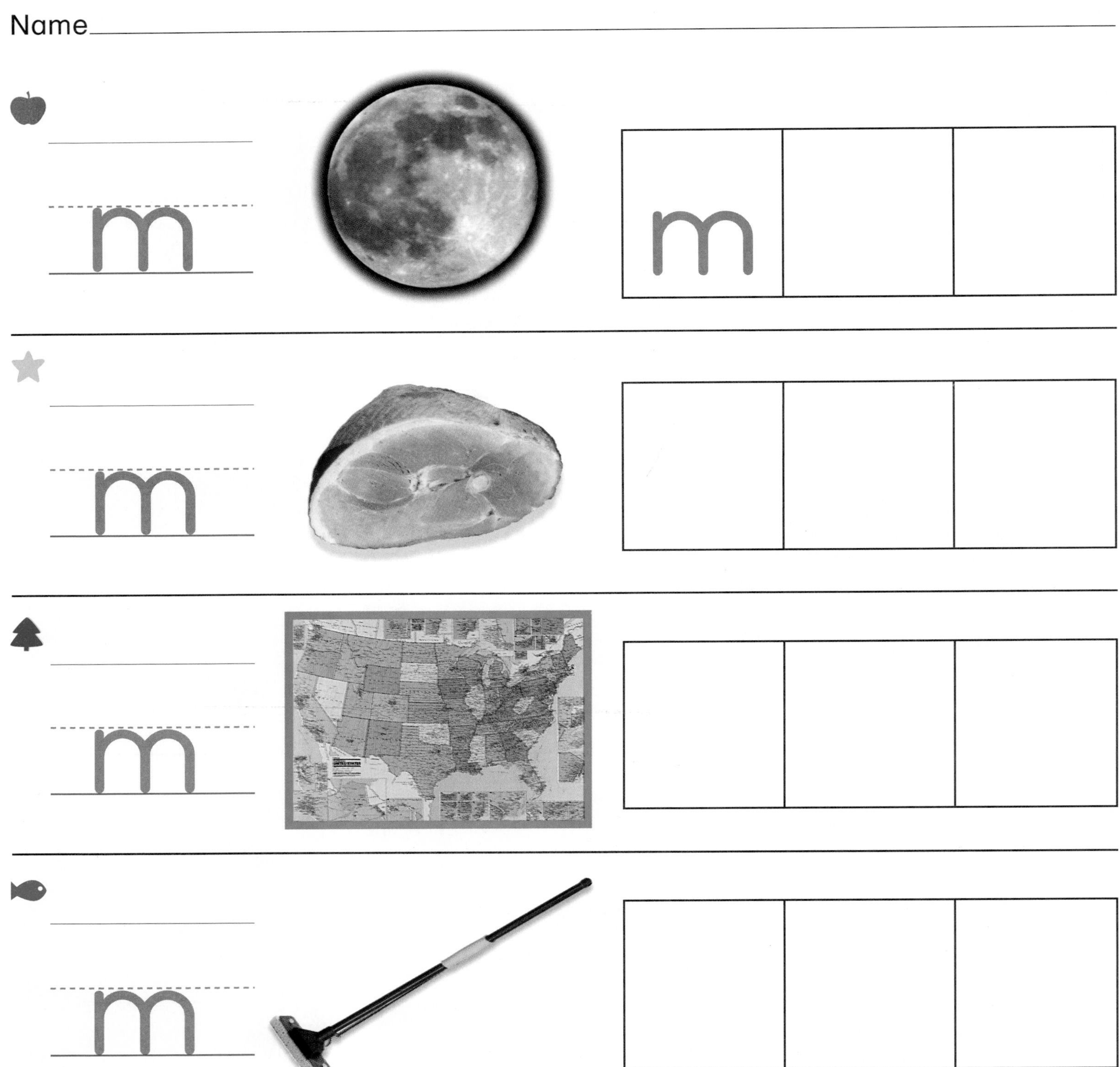

Trace the letter. Say the word that names each picture. Write the letter in the correct box to show if you hear the sound /m/ at the beginning, middle, or the end of the word.

Name ______________________________

is

Sam is sad.

Nan is mad.

Dan is a man.

That is my dad.

Read the sentences. • Then draw a line under the word *is* in each sentence.

Name ____________________

S a m

Sam

d a m

m a n

m a d

Blend the sounds and say the name. Write the name. Draw a circle around the picture that goes with the name.

That man is my dad!

I Am Sam!

Is that man Dad?

I am Sam!

Is that Sam?

Dad?

Is that Dan?

I am Dan!

Name ____________________

Think about the story "I Am Sam!" • In each row, circle the picture that shows something from the story.

Name

N a n — Nan

m a n

m a d

s a d

Blend the sounds and say the name. Write the name. Draw a circle around the picture that goes with the name. Blend the sounds and say the word. Write the word. Draw a circle around the picture that goes with the word.

Name ____________________

I am Sam.

Is that Dad and Dan?

Dad is that man.

That is Dad.

Draw a circle around the word *I*. Draw a circle around the word *and*.
Draw a circle around the word *is*. Draw a circle around the word *that*.

Ii

Name________________________________

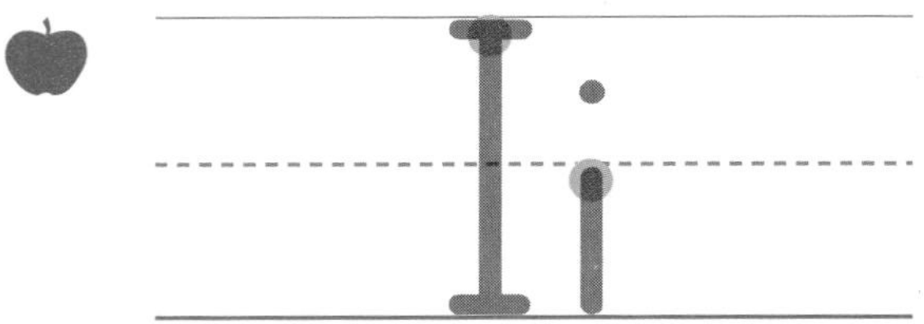

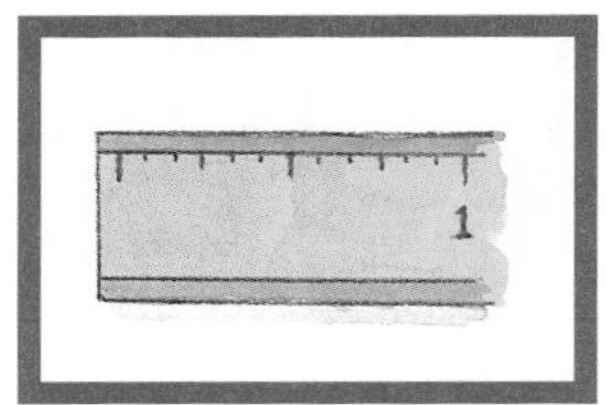

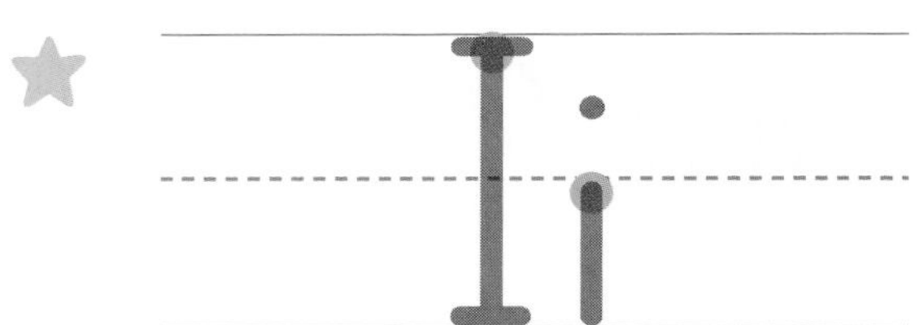

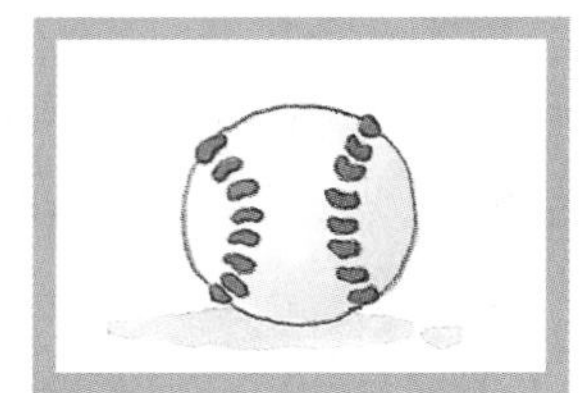

Write the letters *Ii.* • Say the word that names each picture. • Listen for the sound at the beginning of each word. • Draw a circle around each picture whose name begins with the same sound as *igloo*.

Name ______________________________

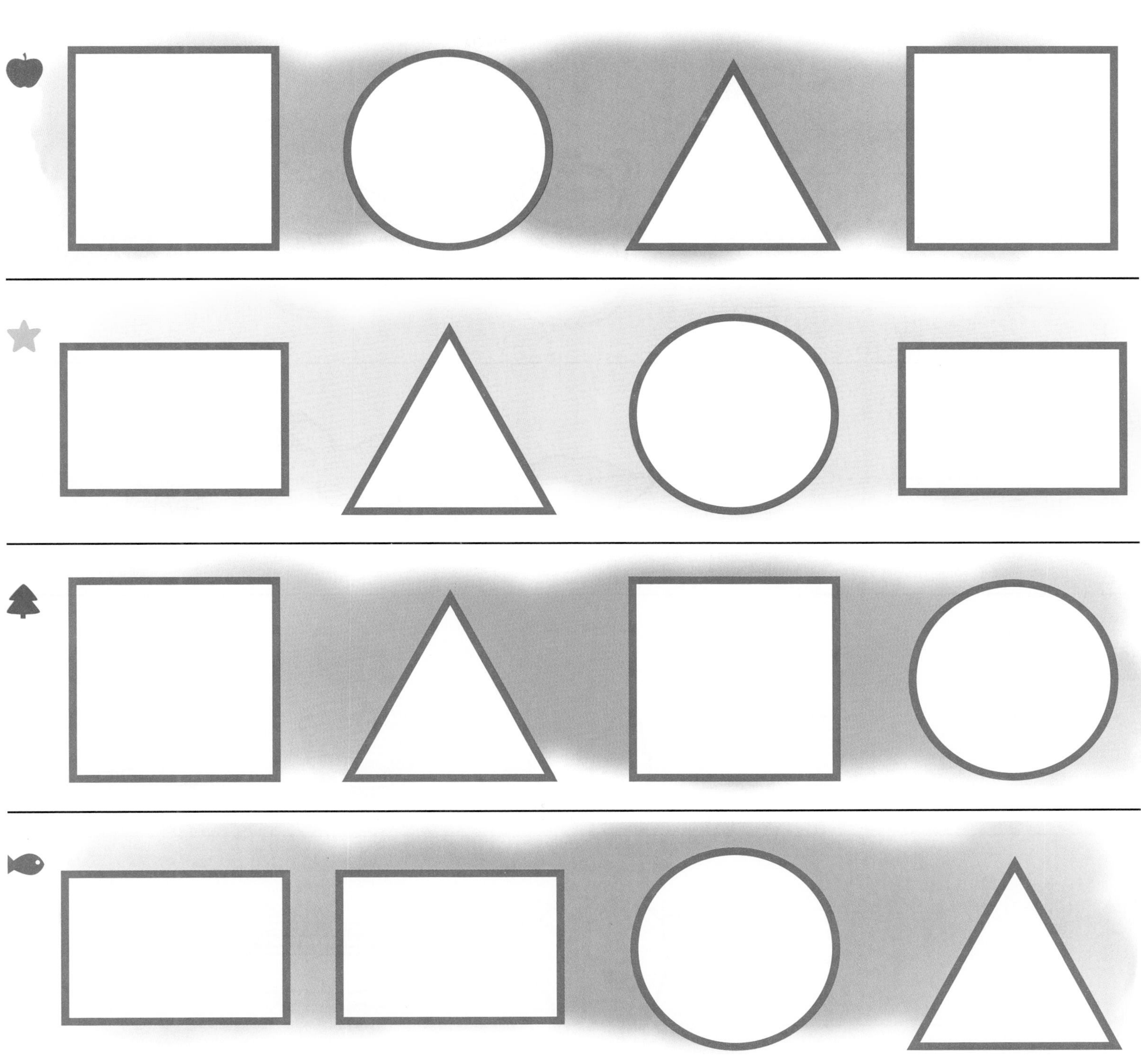

Color the shapes that are the same in each row.

Name________________________________

Write the letter *i*. • Say the word that names each picture. • Listen for the sound in the middle of each word. • Circle each picture whose name has the same middle sound as *pig*.

Name ______________________________

Look at the pictures in each row. Draw a circle around the picture that does not belong.

Name

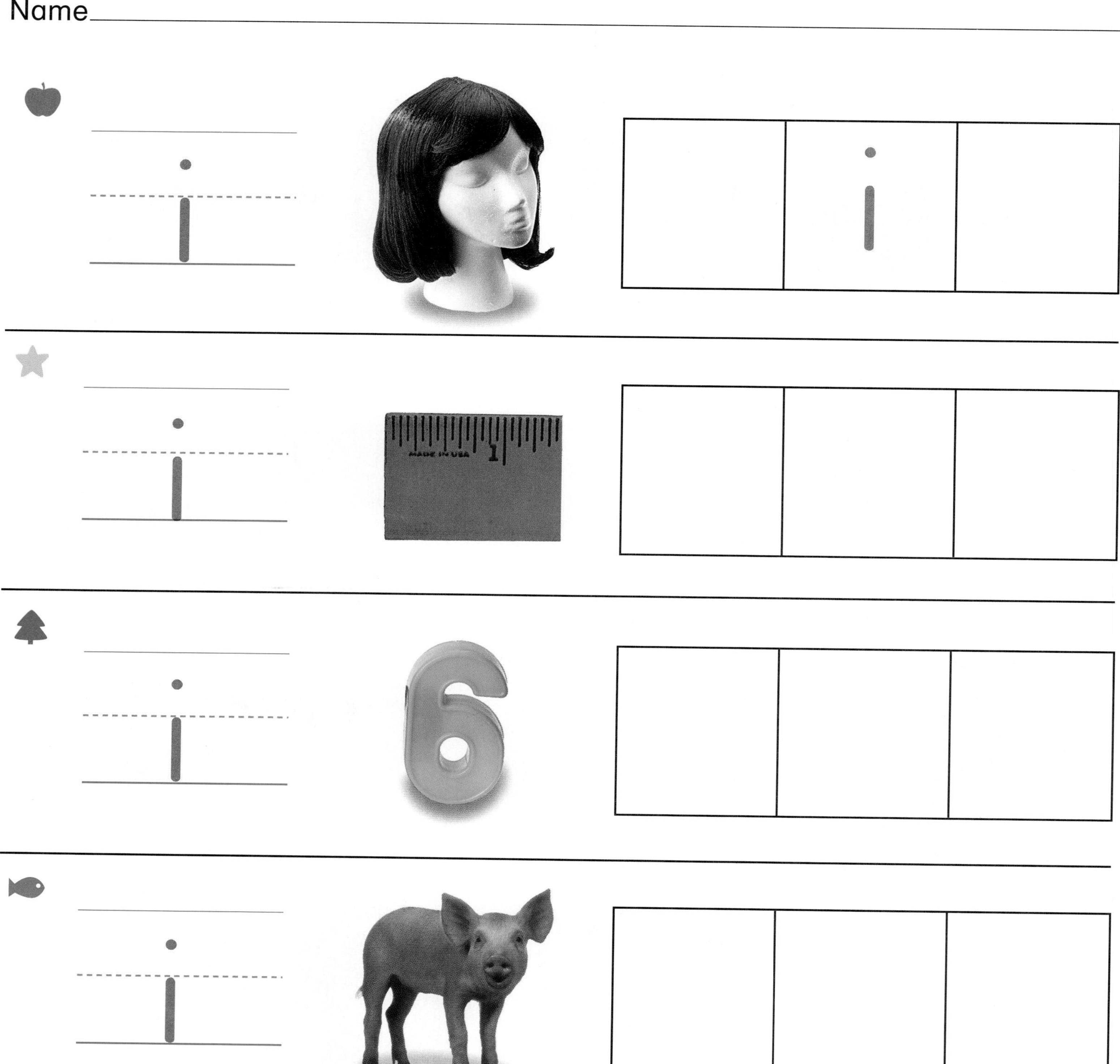

Trace the letter. Say the name of the picture. Write the letter in the correct box to show if you hear the sound /i/ at the beginning, the middle, or the end of the word.

Name________________________________

said

Dan said, "I am Dan."

Nan said, "I am Nan."

Dad said, "I am Dad."

Sam said, "I am Sam."

Read the sentences. • Then draw a line under the word *said* in each sentence.

Name________________________________

i n

in

d i m

d i d

S i d

Blend the sounds and say the word. Write the word. Use the word aloud in a sentence.

That is a .

Sid Said

Min said, “That is .”

Min said, “That is .”

Sid said, “That is .”

Sam said, “That is .”

Sam said, “That is .”

Sid said, “That is .”

Name ____________________

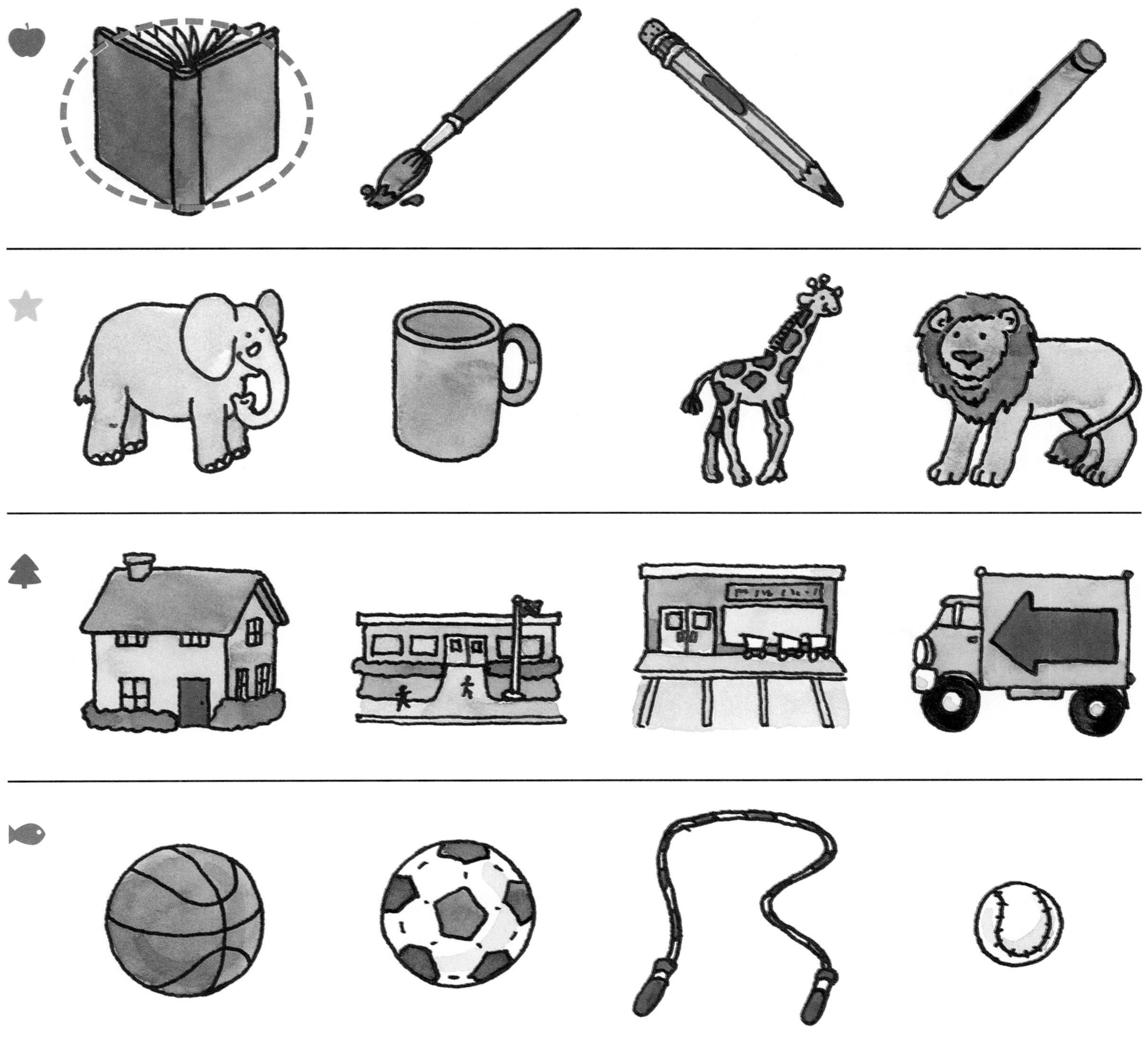

Look at the pictures in each row. • Draw a circle around the picture that does not belong.

Name ____________________

S i d

Sid

d i m

m a n

s a d

Look at the name. Blend the sounds and say the name. Write the name. Use the name aloud in a sentence. Look at each word. Blend the sounds and say the word. Write the word. Use the word aloud in a sentence.

Name______________________________

Nan said, "Sam is sad."

Sam said, "Am I sad?"

"I am ," said Sam.

Read each sentence. Draw a line under the word *is*. Draw a line under the word *said*. Draw a line under the word *I*.

Name________________________________

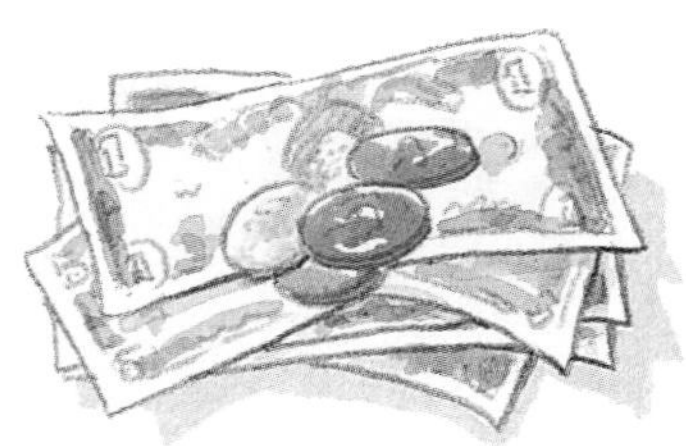

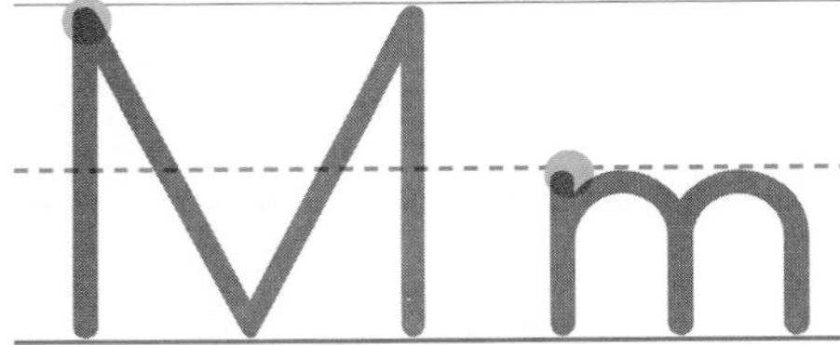

Say the name of each picture. • Then write the letter that stands for the sound you hear at the beginning of the picture name.

Name ____

2	
4	
5	
7	
10	

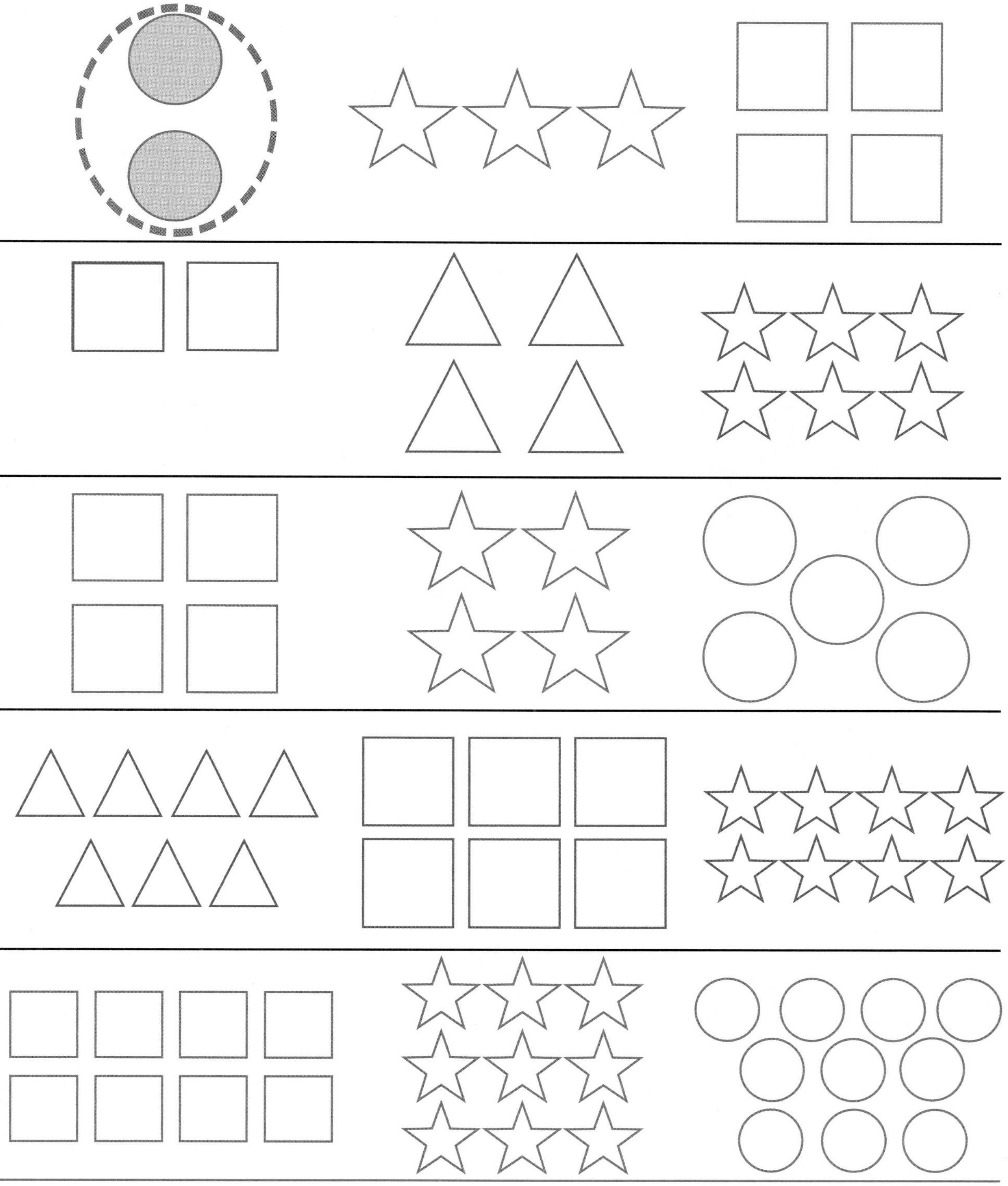

Draw a circle around the group of objects in each row that shows the number on the left. Then, color the circles green, and the triangles red.

Name ____________________

___d

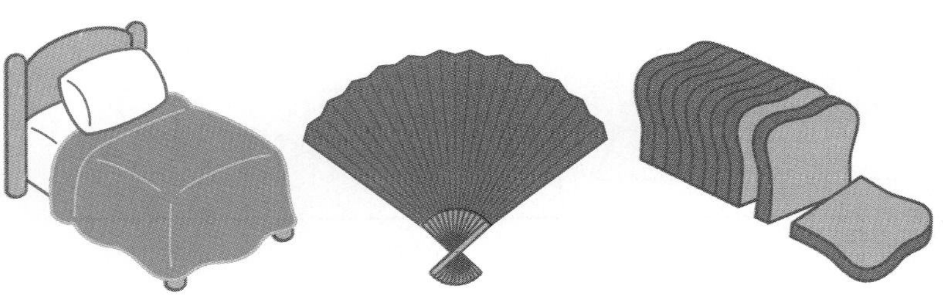

___d

___m

___m

Say the name of the picture. If you hear the sound /d/ at the end of the word, circle the picture. If you hear the sound /m/ at the end of the word, circle the picture.

Name ______________________________

Think about the story "Warthogs in the Kitchen." • In each row, circle the pictures that show something from the story.

Name

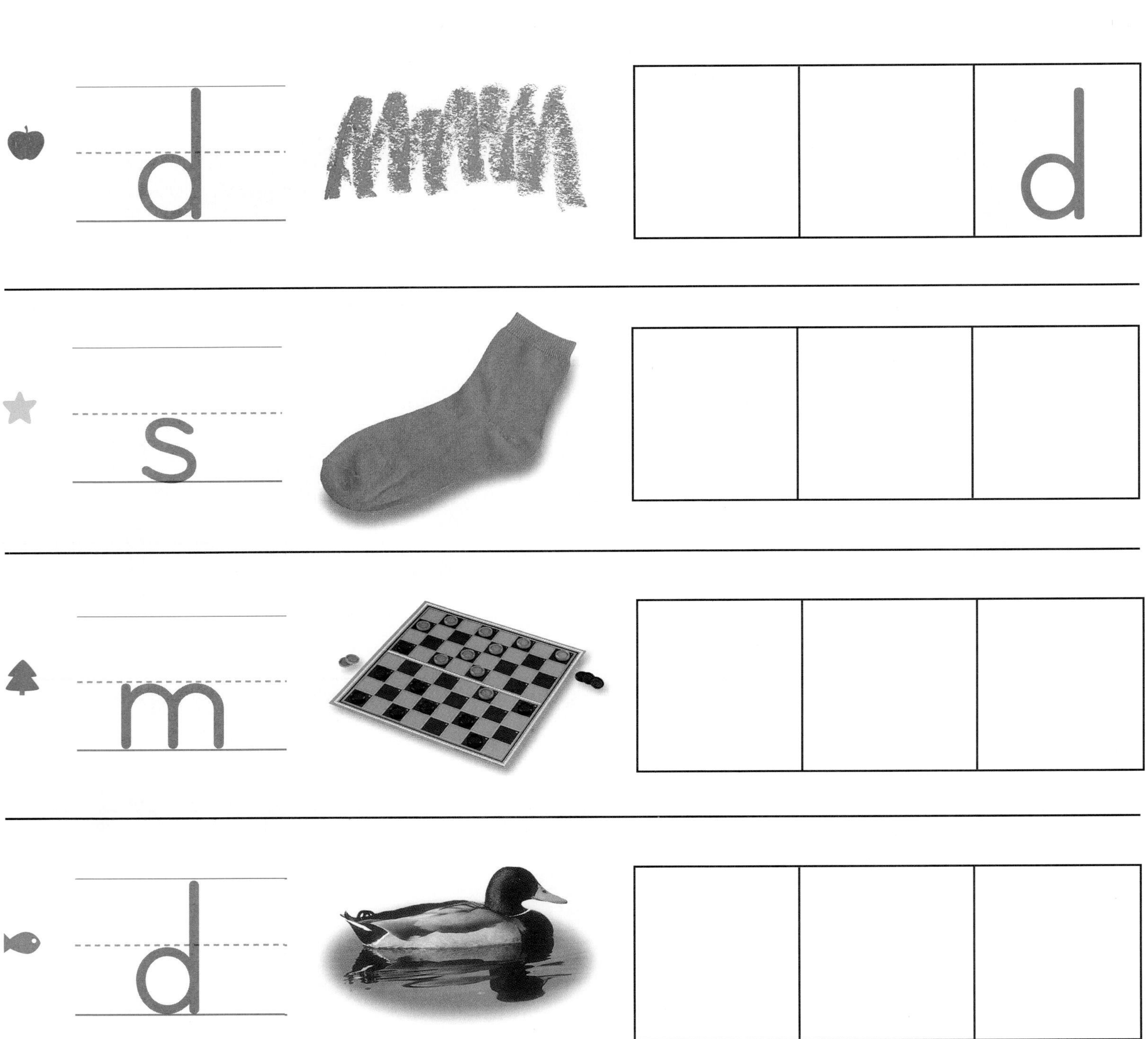

Trace the letter. Say the word that names the picture. Then, write the letter in the correct box to show if you hear the sound /d/, /s/, or /m/ at the beginning, the middle, or the end of the word.

Name ______________________________

said is 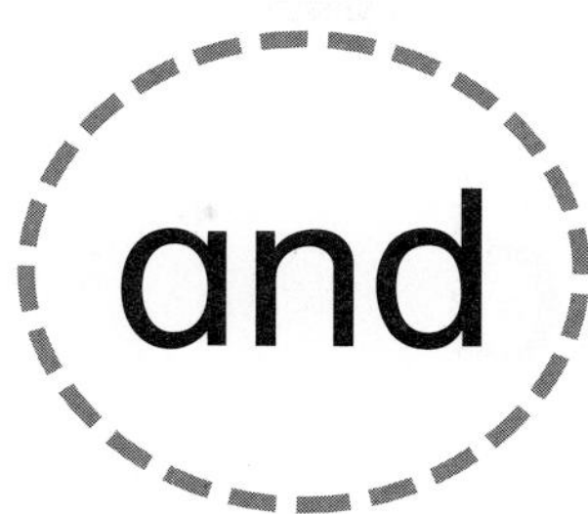 and I

and I said is

said and is I

is I and said

Read the words. Draw a circle around the word *and.* Draw a circle around the word *I.* Draw a circle around the word *is.* Draw a circle around the word *said.*

Name ____________________

d i d

did

S i d

s a d

D a d

Blend the sounds and say the word. Write the word. Use the word aloud in a sentence. Blend the sounds and say the name. Write the name. Use the name aloud in a sentence.

I am Sam and I am .

Is Sam Mad?

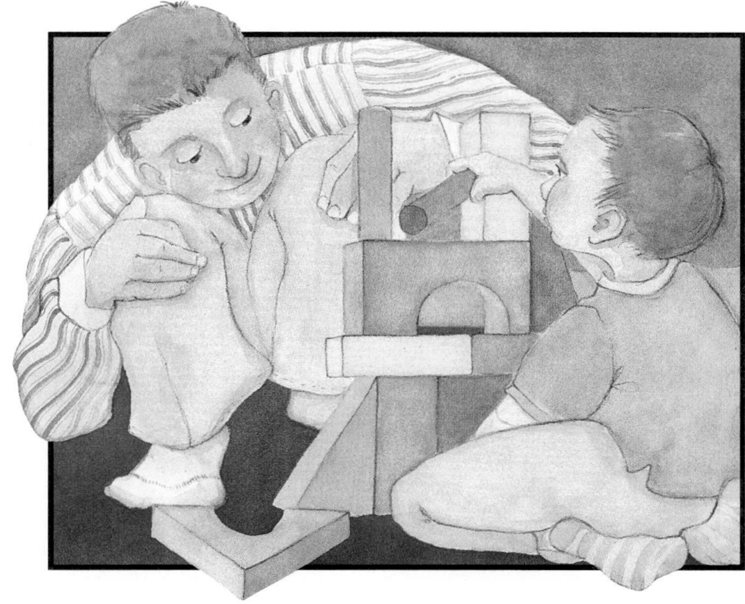

Dad said that I am mad.

Sid said that I am mad.

Nan said that I am mad.

Am I mad?

McGraw-Hill School Division

Dan said that I am mad.

Min said that I am mad.

Name____

Look at the pictures in each row. • Draw a circle around the picture that does not belong.

Name ____________________

mad sad

sad

in am

man mad

Sid Nan

Look at the picture. Read the words. Draw a circle around the word that goes with the picture. Write the word. Look at the picture. Read the names. Draw a circle around the name that goes with the picture. Write the name.

Name ________________________________

said	that	said	my
is	is	said	my
and	a	is	and
I	the	and	I

Say the first word in the row. • Draw a circle around the word where you see it in the same row.

Name

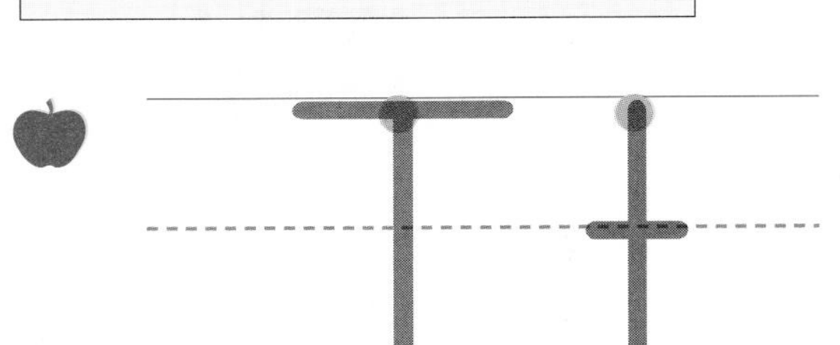

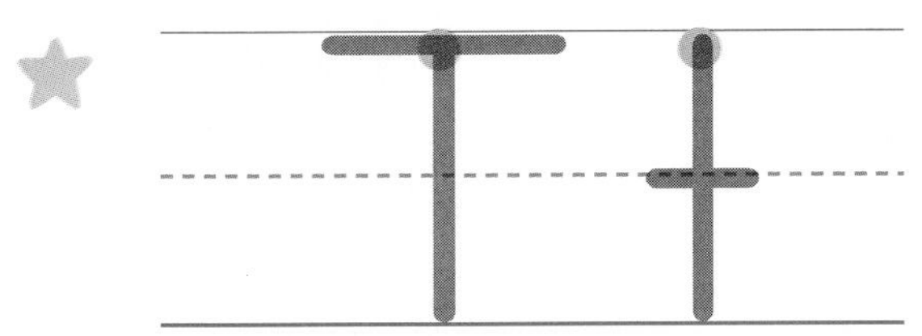

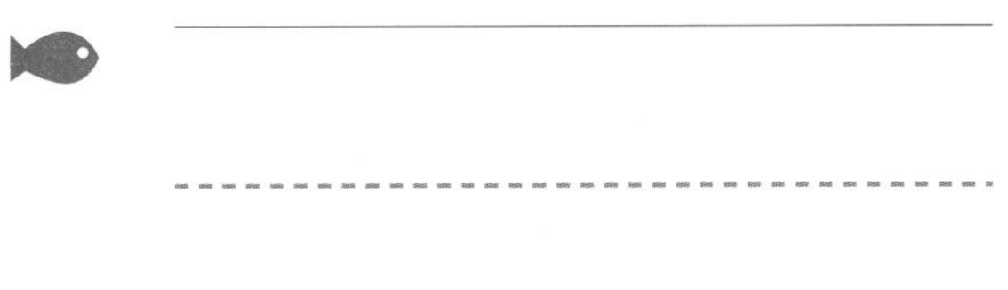

Write the letters *Tt.* • Say the word that names each picture. • Listen for the sound at the beginning of each word. • Draw a circle around each picture whose name begins with the same sound as *tiger.*

Name ____________________

- Draw a circle around the person who is tall. Draw a line under the person who is short.
- Draw a circle around the item that is heavy. Draw a line under the item that is light.
- Draw a circle around the person who is high. Draw a line under the person who is low.

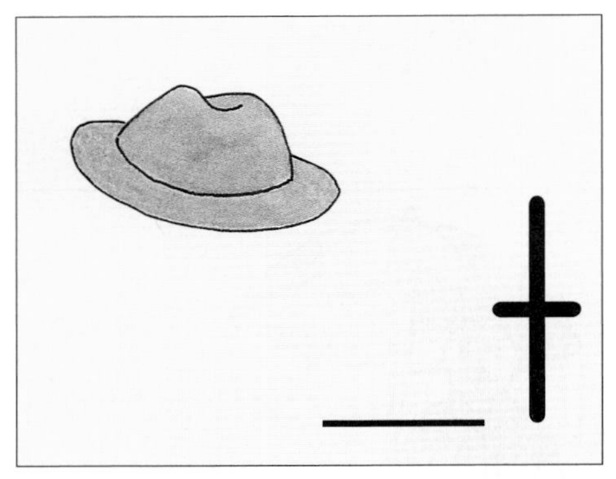

Name____________________

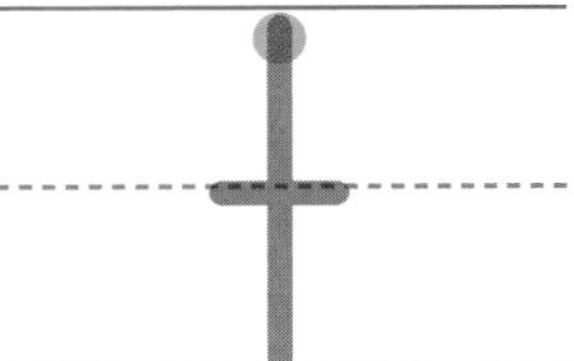

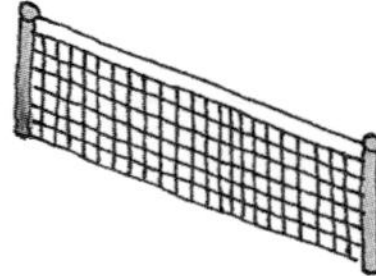

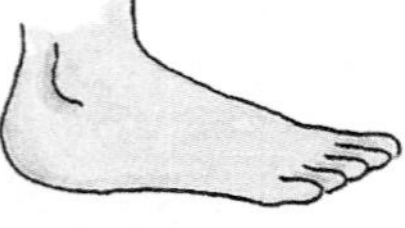

Say the name of each picture. • Circle the pictures whose names have the same ending sound as *hat*. • Write the letter.

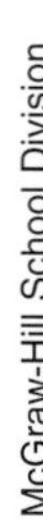

Name ________________________________

Look at the pictures in each row. Circle the one that shows something that might really happen. Draw a line under the picture that is make-believe.

Name ____________________

t

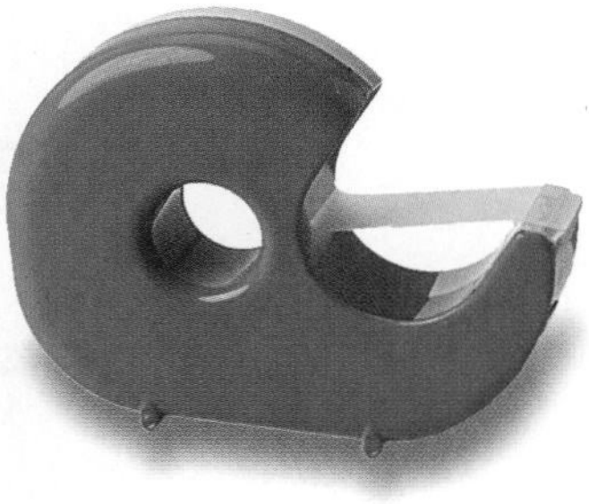

t		

t

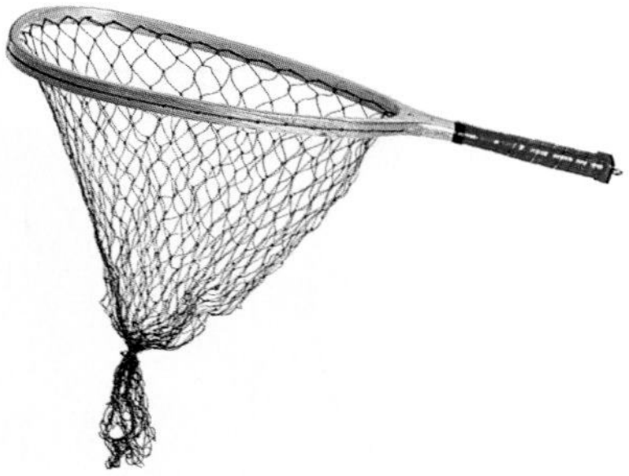

t

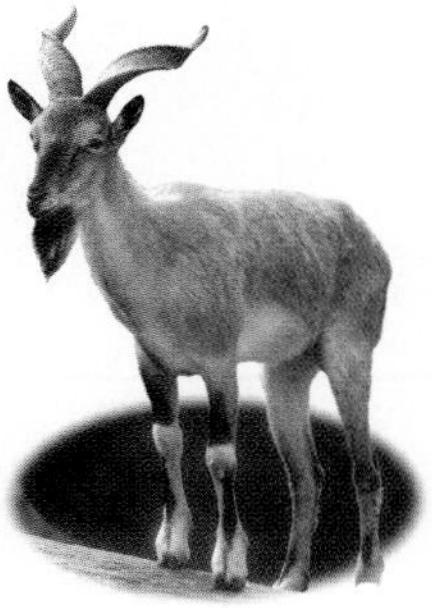

t

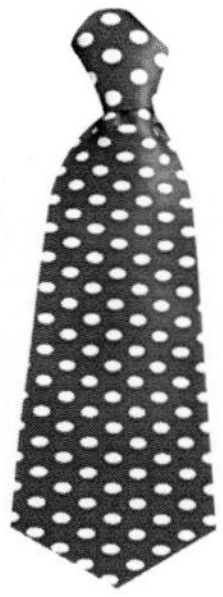

Trace the letter. Say the word that names the picture. Write the letter in the correct box to show if you hear the sound /t/ at the beginning, middle, or the end of the word.

Name ______________________________

we

We sit at the  .

We sit in the  .

We sit in the  .

We sit in my  .

Read the sentences. • Draw a line under the word *we* in each sentence.

Name________________________________

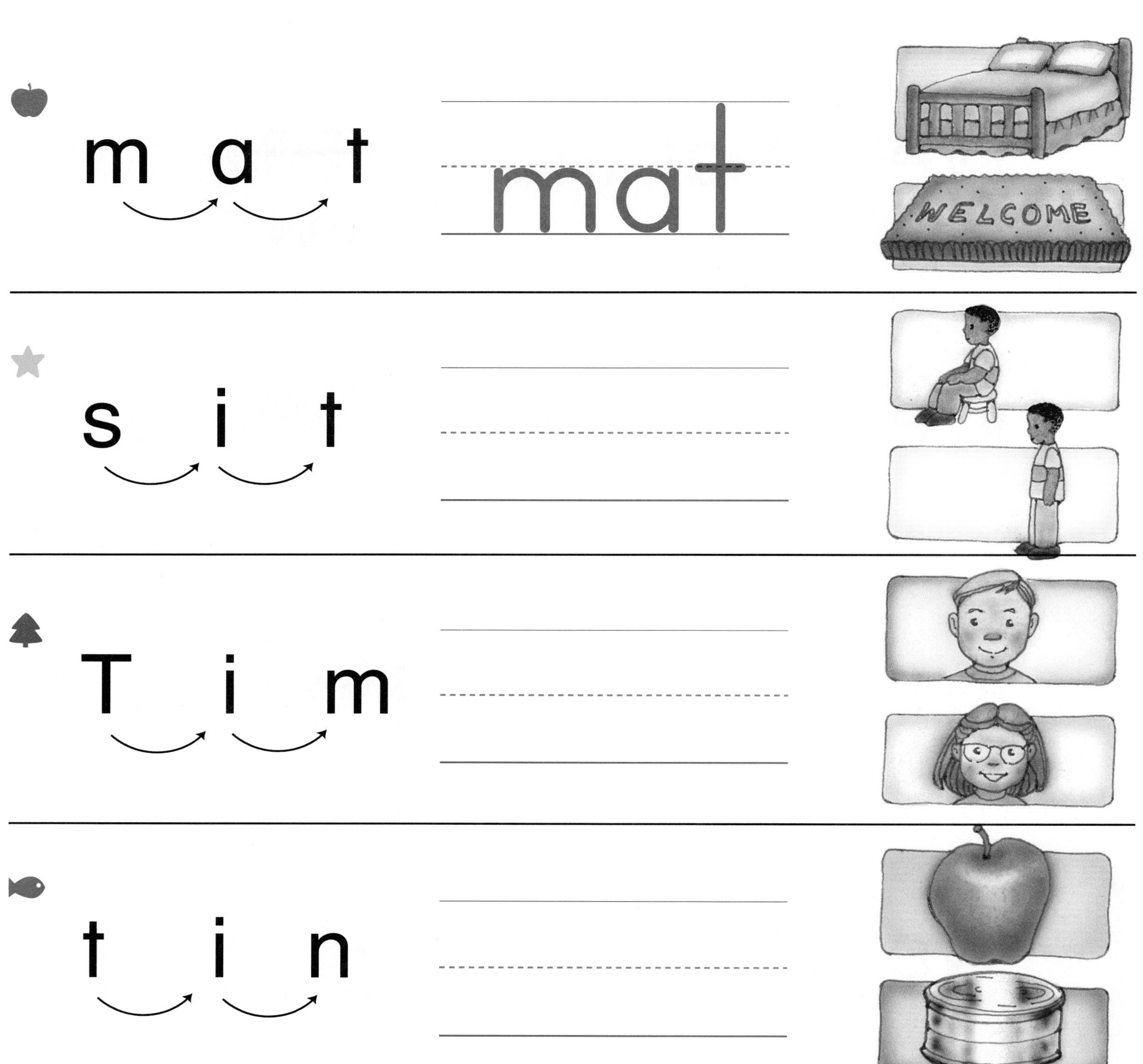

Blend the sounds and say the word. • Write the word. • Draw a circle around the picture that goes with the word.

Tam sat.

8

That Tam!

I said, "Sit, Tam!"

6

Tim sat.

3

I said, "Sit, Tim."

We said, "Tam, sit!"

I said, "Sit, Tam."

"Sit, Tam!" I said.

Name ______________________________

Look at each row of pictures. Draw a circle around the picture that shows something that might really happen. Draw a line under the picture that is make-believe.

Name

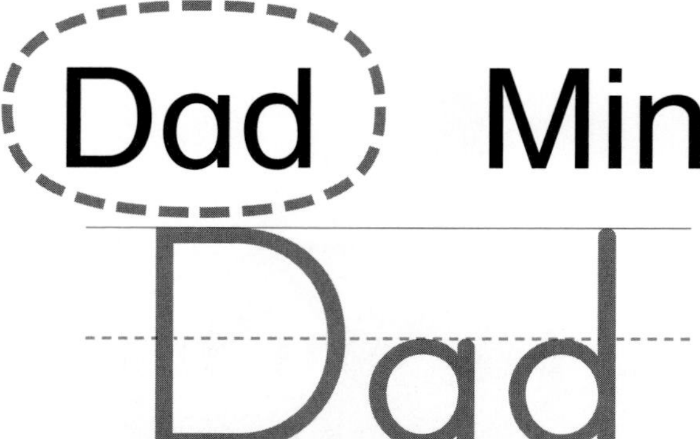

sit mat

dam tin

Nan Sid

Draw a circle around the word that goes with the picture. • Say the word. • Then write the word.

Name______________________________

We said, "Is that the mat?"

We said, "Did Tim sit?"

We said, "Tim sat."

Read the sentences. Then do the following: ● Draw a circle around the word *the*. ★ Draw a circle around the word *said*. ▲ Draw a circle around the word *we*.

Name ______________________________

Cc

Cc

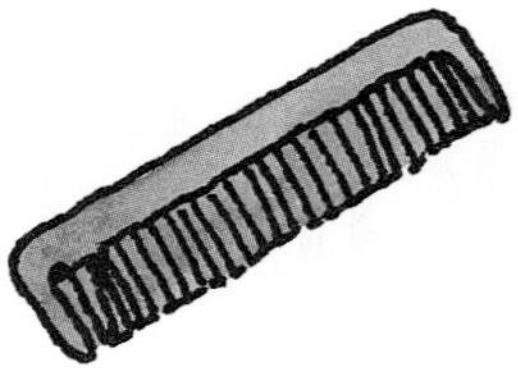

Write the letters *Cc*. • Say the word that names each picture. • Listen for the sound at the beginning of each word. • Draw a circle around each picture whose name begins with the same sound as *car*.

Name____

Draw apples in the tall tree. • Color the short tree green. • Find the bird that is high. • Color it blue. • Find the bird that is low. • Color it red. • Draw a line under something that is heavy. • Draw a circle around something that is light.

Cc

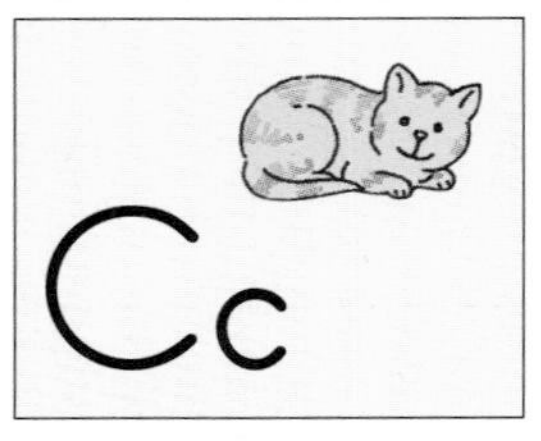

Name ____________________

Cc

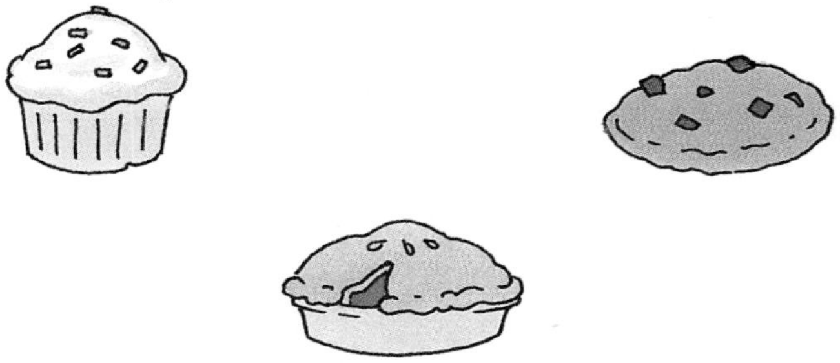

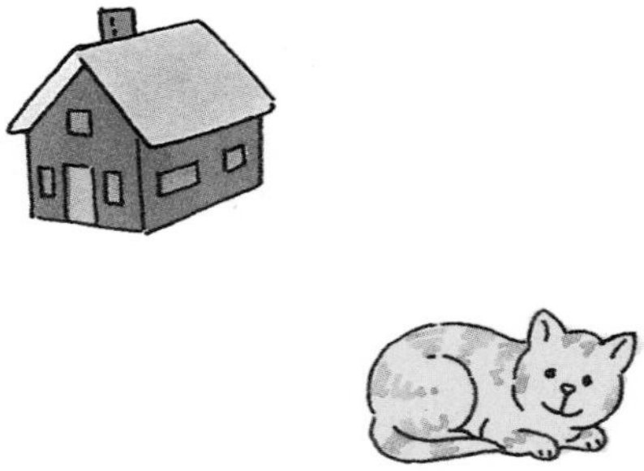

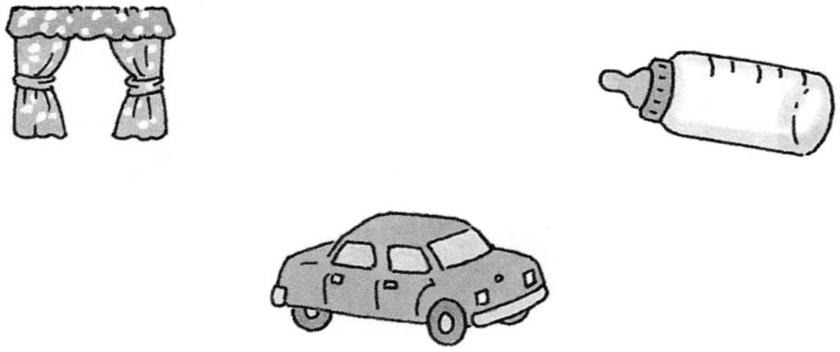

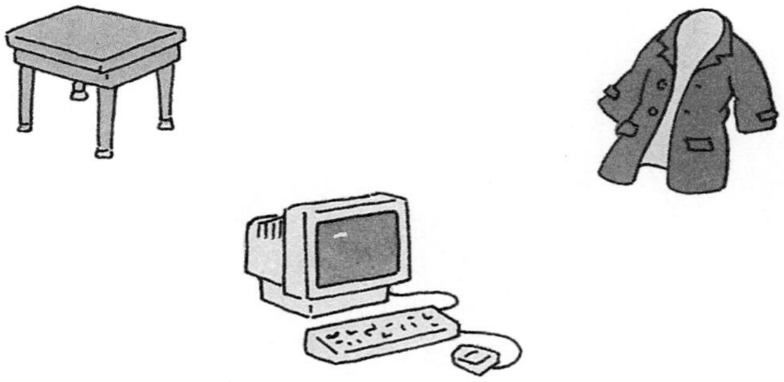

Write the letters *Cc.* • Say the word that names each picture. • Draw a line from the *Cc* to each picture whose name has the same beginning sound as *cat.*

Name ______________________________

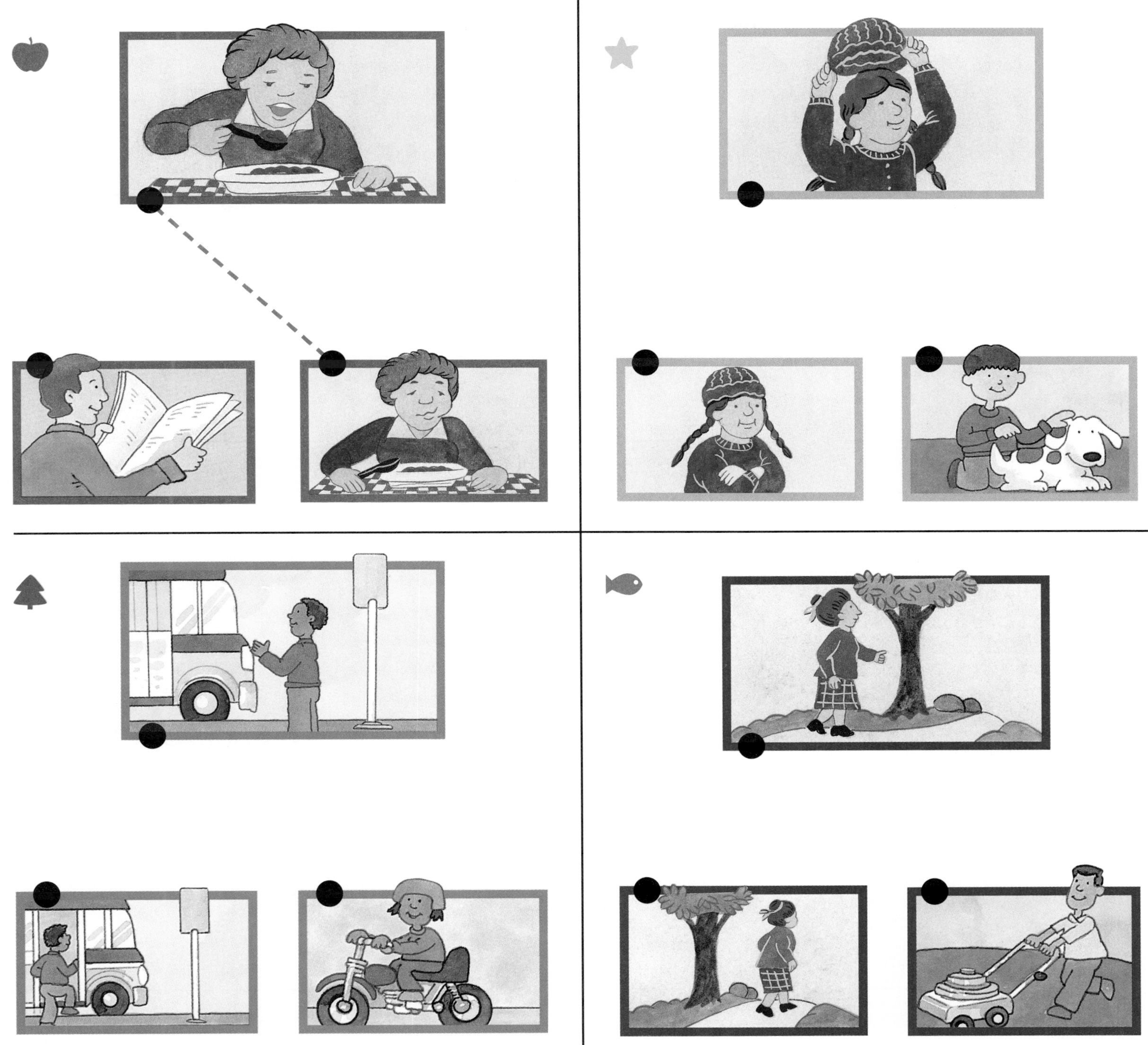

Look at each big picture. Draw a line to the small picture that shows what will happen next.

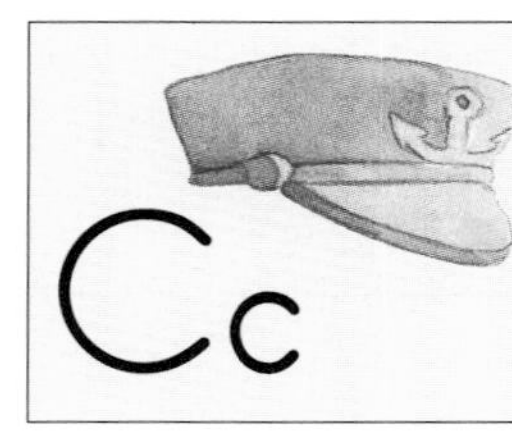

Name______________________________

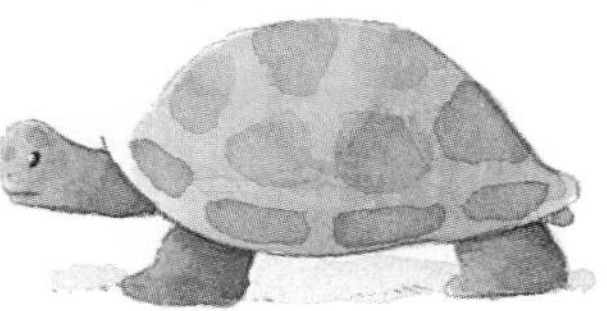

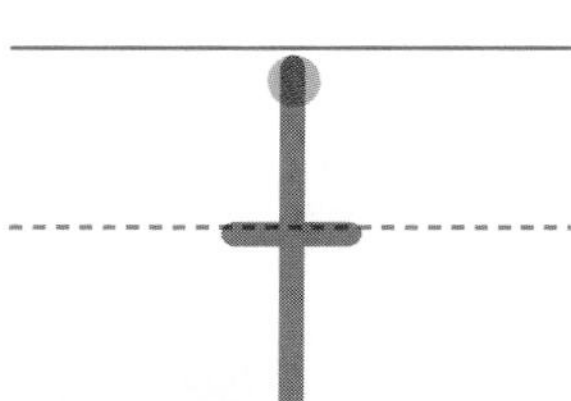

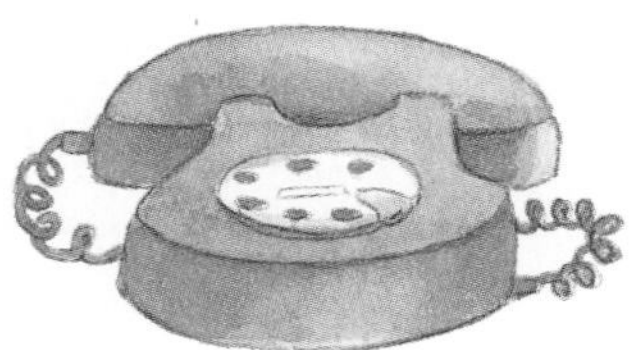

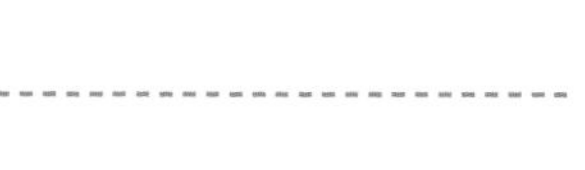

Say the name of each picture. • Under the picture write the letter for the sound you hear at the beginning of the picture name.

Name________________________________ **are**

We are Nan and Tim.

Are we sad?

Are we mad?

We are  .

Read the sentences. • Draw a line under the word *are* in each sentence.

Name ____________________

c a t

cat

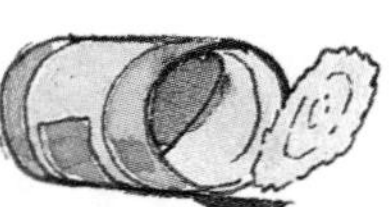

c a n

m a n

m a d

Blend the sounds and say the word. • Write the word. • Draw a circle around the picture that goes with the word.

We are Nat and Min.

Nat Is My Cat

I said, "Sit, Nat."

Nat is my tan cat.

I am Min.

Nat, the cat, sat.

We are Nat and Min.

We can sit and sit.

Name ______________________________

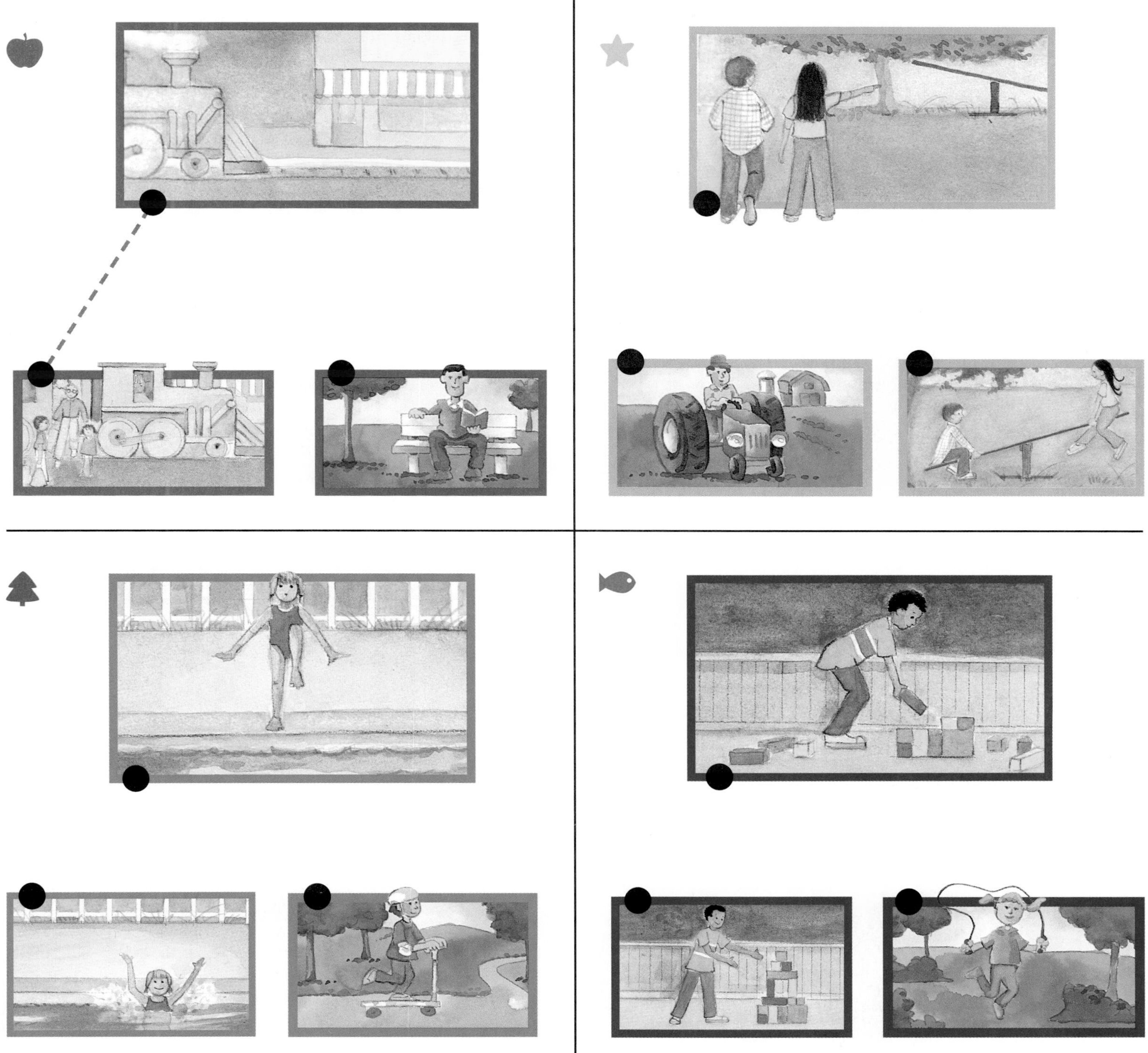

Look at each big picture. Draw a line to the small picture that shows what will happen next.

Name ____________________

sad mad

sad

Tim Nan

can cat

did sit

Draw a circle around the word that names the picture. • Say the word. • Then write the word.

Name ___________________________

We are Nan and Dad.

We are at the mat.

That is Dad.

Read the sentences. Draw a circle around the word *are*. Draw a circle around the word *we*. Draw a circle around the word *is*.

Name ____________________

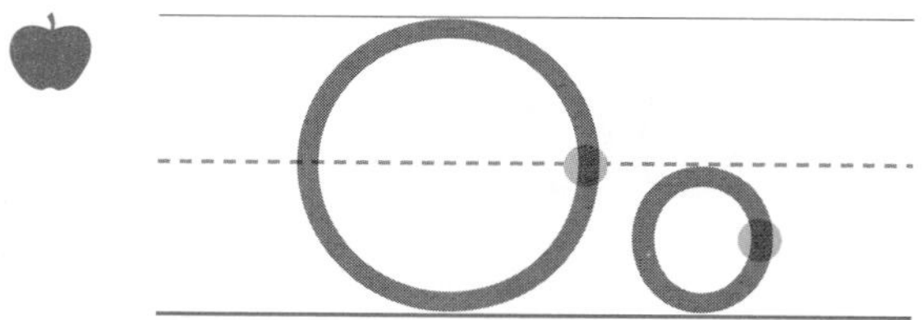

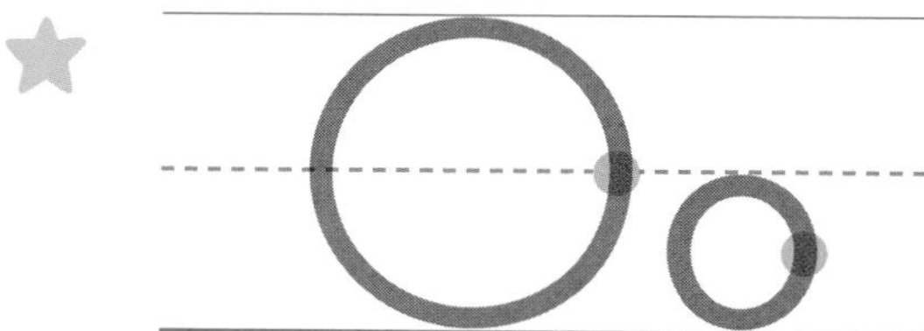

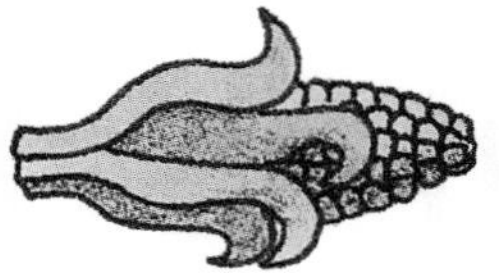

Write the letters *Oo*. • Say the word that names each picture. • Listen for the sound at the beginning of each word. • Draw a circle around each picture whose name begins with the same sound as *octopus*.

Name____

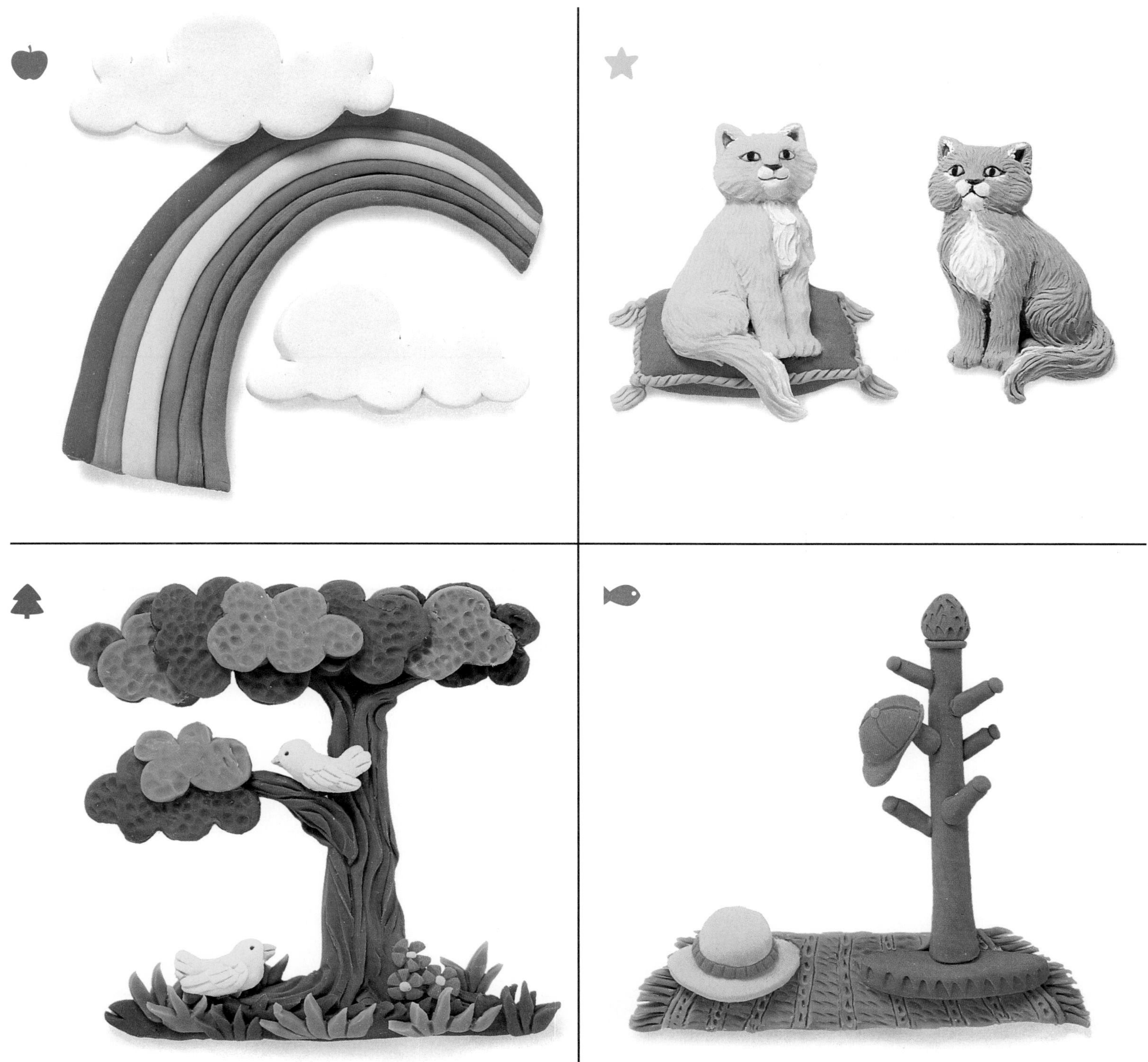

Draw a circle around the cloud that is above the rainbow. Draw a circle around the cat that is on the pillow. Draw a circle around the bird that is below the branch. Draw a circle around the hat that is on the hat stand.

Name

Write the letter *o*. • Say the word that names each picture. • Listen for the sound in the middle of each word. • Circle each picture whose name has the same middle sound as *box*.

Name ______________________________

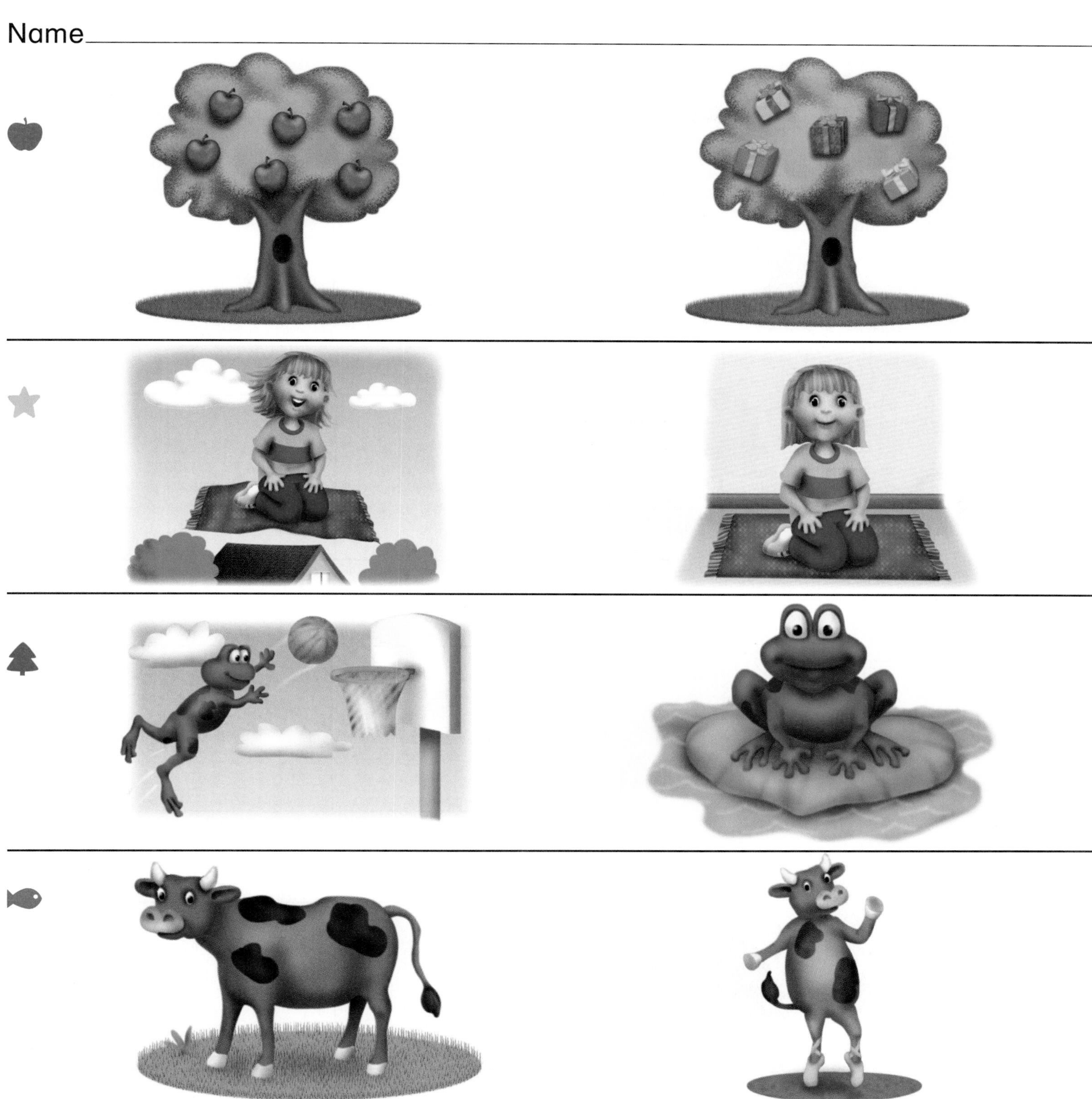

Look at each row of pictures. • Draw a circle around the picture that shows something that might really happen. • Draw a line under the picture that is make-believe.

Name

o

o

o

o

o

Trace the letter. Say the word that names the picture. Write the letter in the correct box to show if you hear the sound /o/ at the beginning, the middle, or the end of the word.

Name ______________________

you

Dad said, “Is that you?”

Nan said, “Is that you?”

Tom said, “It is not you.”

Mom said, “It is you!”

Read the sentences. • Draw a line under the word *you* in each sentence.

Name ____

o n

on

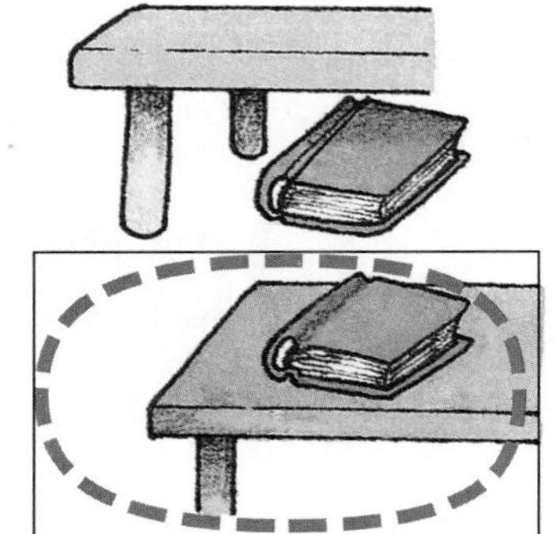

d o t

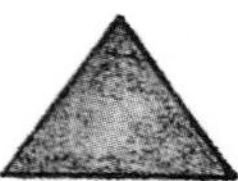

M o m

c o t

Blend the sounds and say the word. • Write the word. • Draw a circle around the picture that goes with the word.

The cat is on a dot!

On a Dot

You are not on a dot.

Tom is on a dot.

Don is on a dot.

Are you sad?

Mom is on a dot.

Dad is on a dot.

Name______________________________

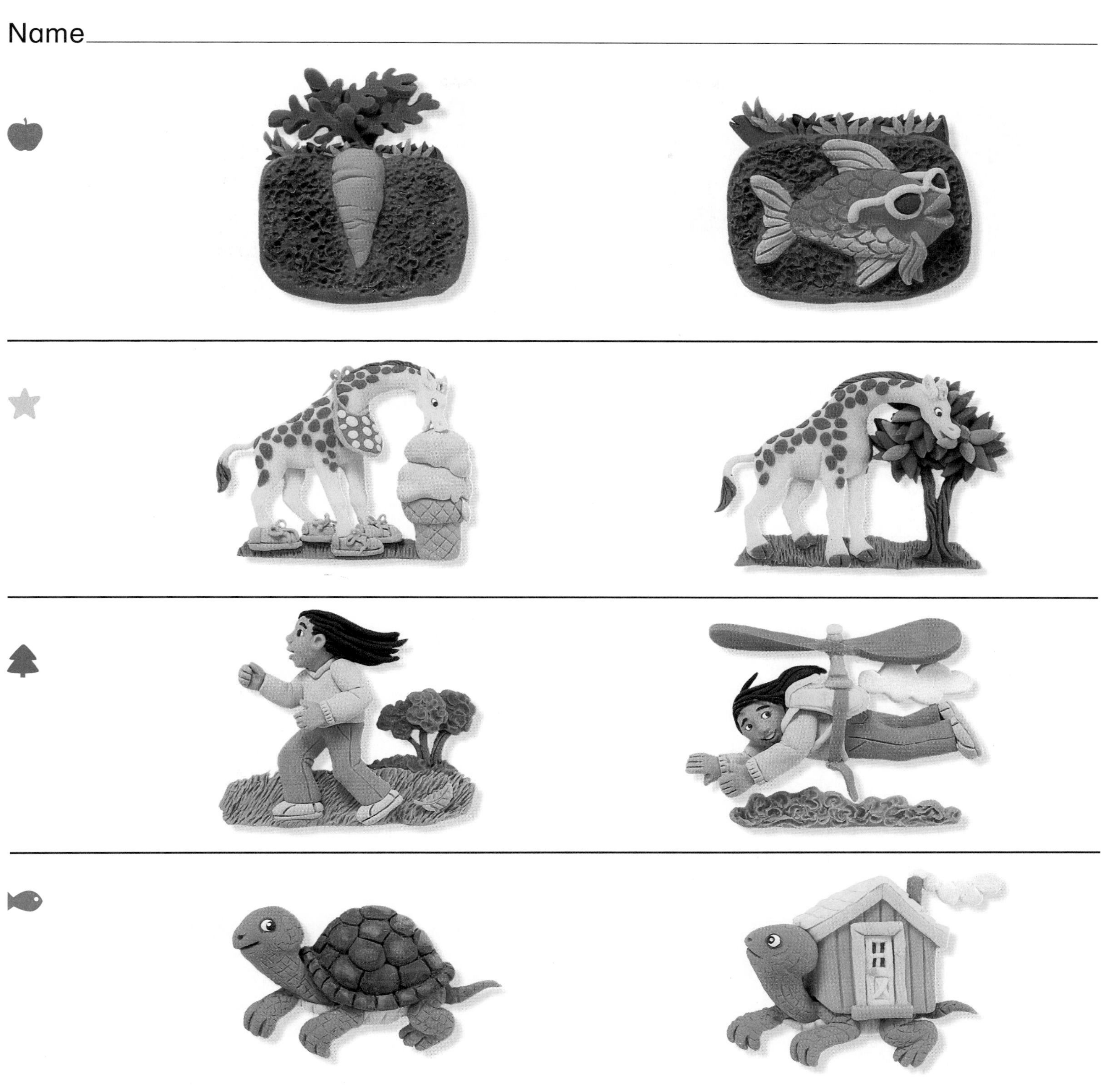

Look at each row of pictures. • Circle the picture that shows something that might really happen. • Draw a line under the picture that is make-believe.

Name ______________________________

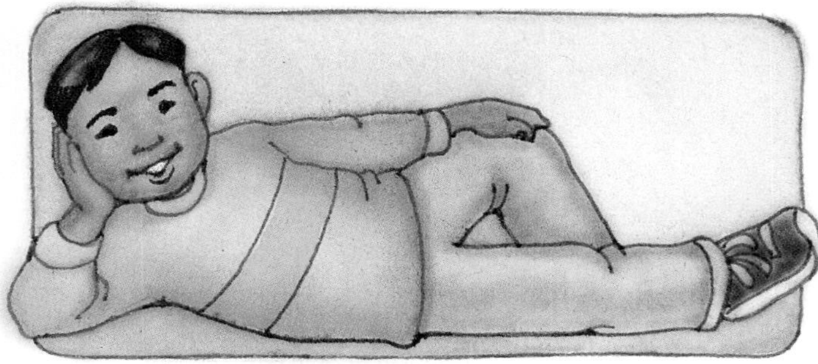

Nan Tim

Tim

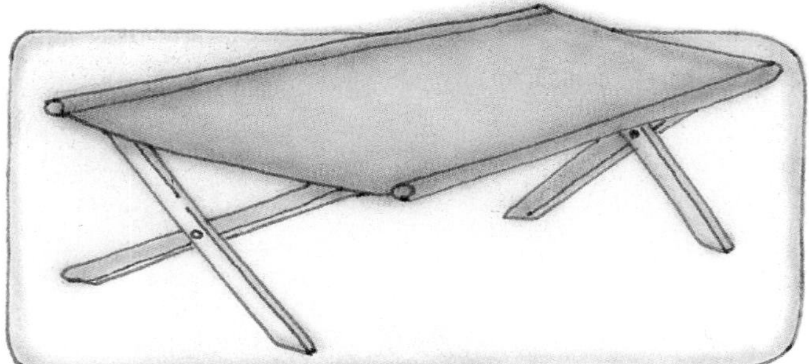

cot tot

Mom Tom

tan can

Draw a circle around the word that names the picture. • Say the word. • Then write the word.

Name____

You are on the mat.

My cat is on that mat.

You can sit on my cot.

Read the sentences. Then do the following: ● Draw a circle around the word *you*. Draw a line under the word *are*. ★ Draw a circle around the word *that*. ▲ Draw a circle around the word *my*.

Ff

Name ____________________

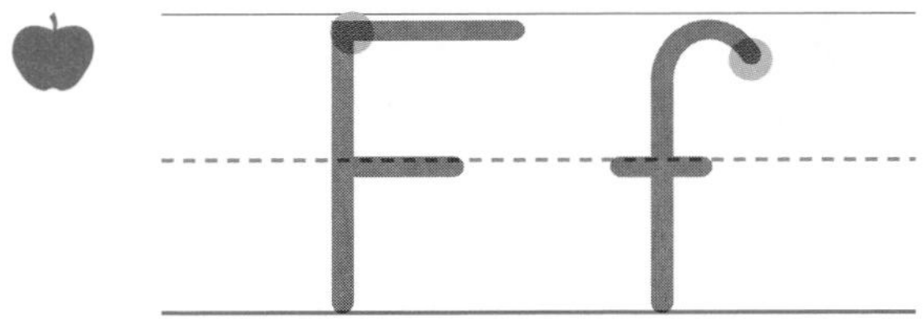

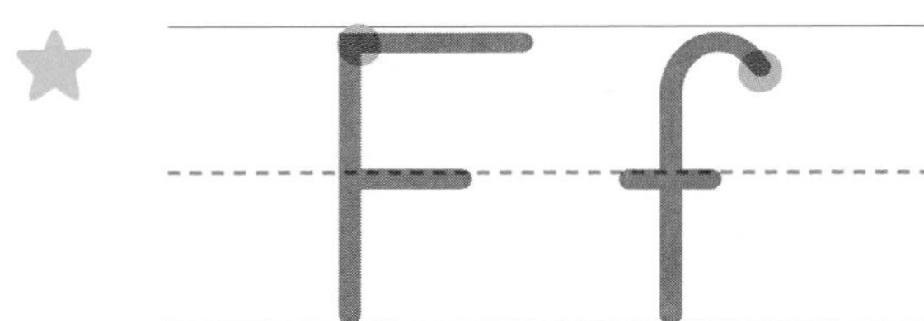

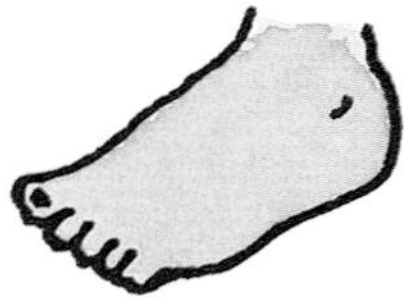

Write the letters *Ff*. • Say the word that names each picture. • Listen for the sound at the beginning of each word. • Draw a circle around each picture whose name begins with the same sound as *fish*.

Name ____

Point to the milk container on the top shelf. • Point to the lettuce on the middle shelf. • Point to the eggs on the bottom shelf. • Draw an apple on the top shelf. • Draw a banana on the middle shelf. • Draw an orange on the bottom shelf.

Name ____________________

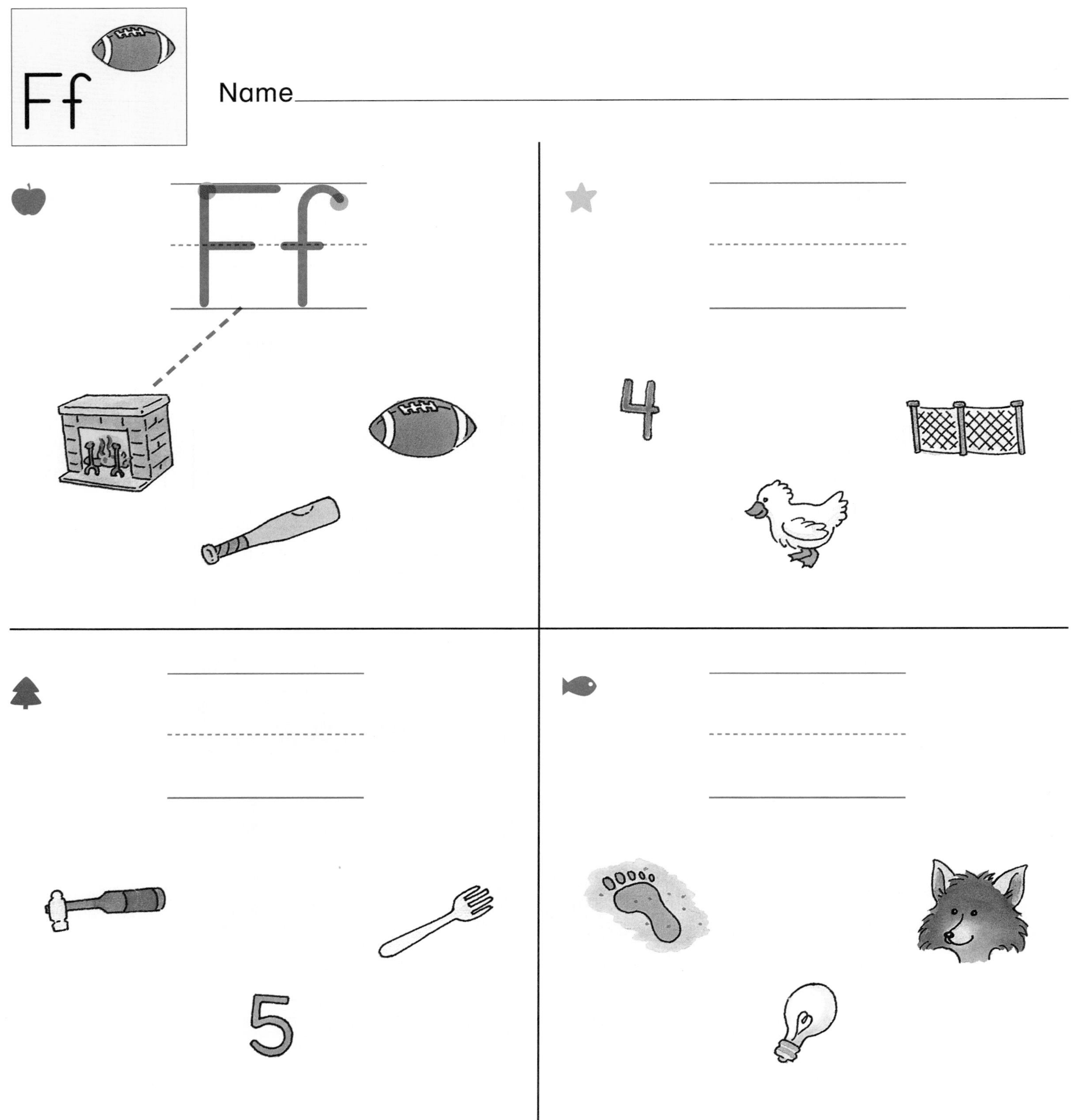

Write the letters *Ff*. Then draw a line from *Ff* to each picture whose name begins with the same sound as *football*.

Name

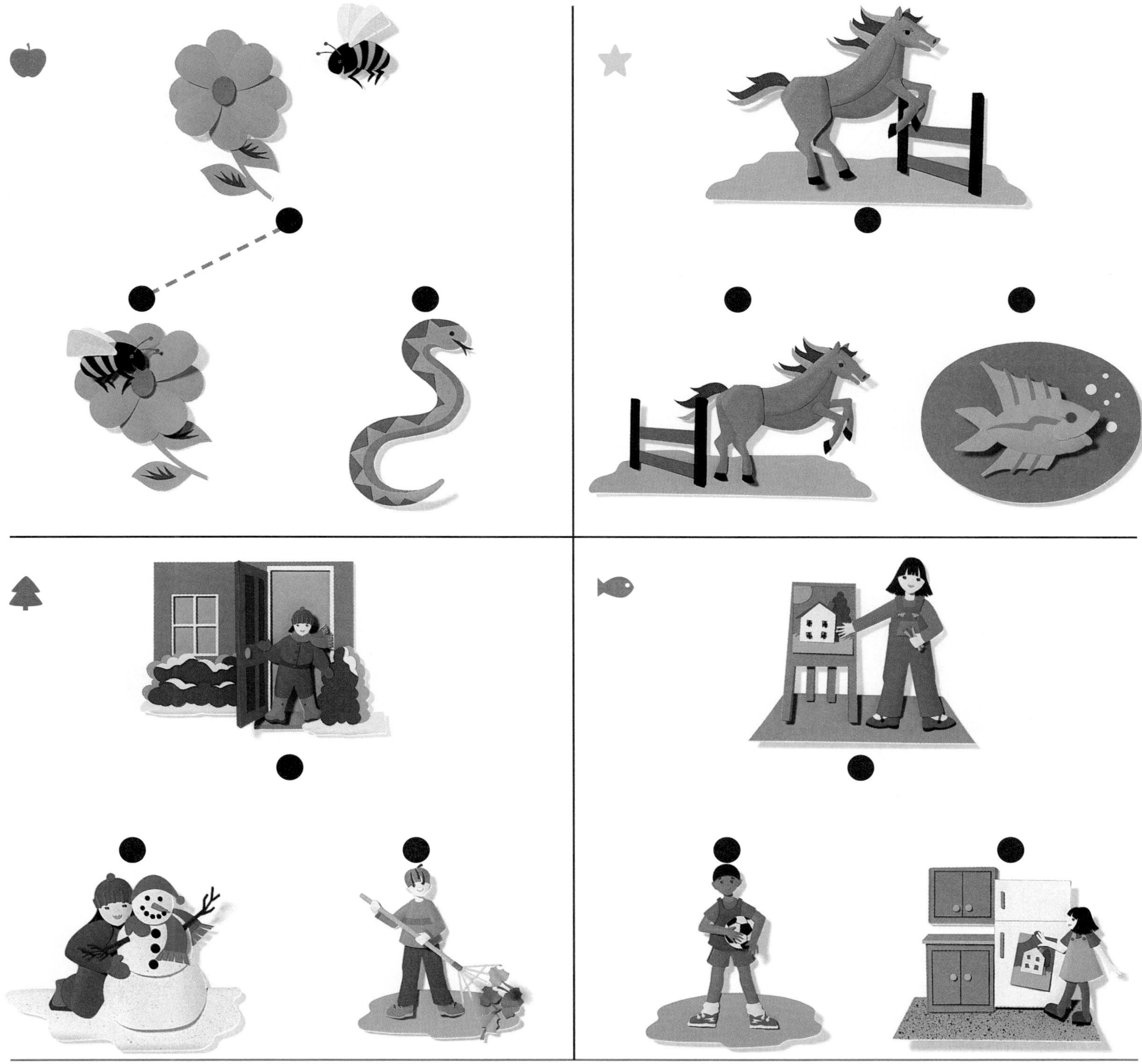

Look at the top picture in each box. Draw a line to the picture below it that shows what will happen next.

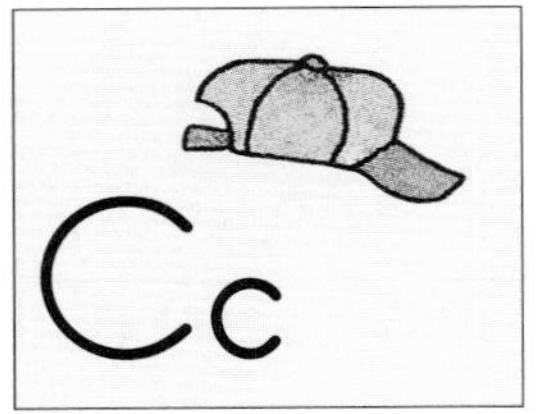

Name ______________________

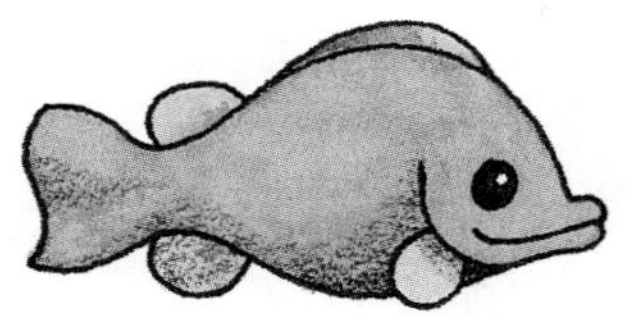

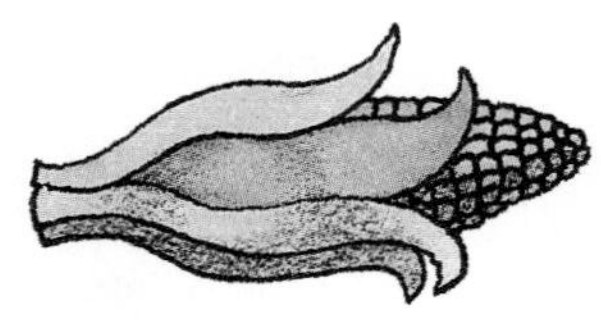

f

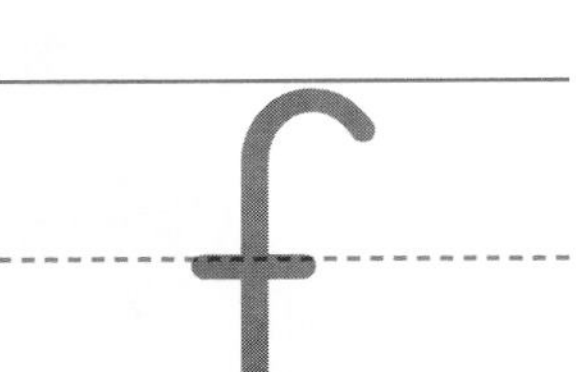

Say the name of each picture. • Under the picture write the letter for the sound you hear at the beginning of the picture name.

Name____

have

Can I have a cat?

You can have a cat.

Can I have a tan cat?

I have a tan cat!

Read the sentences. • Draw a line under the word *have* in each sentence.

Name

i f

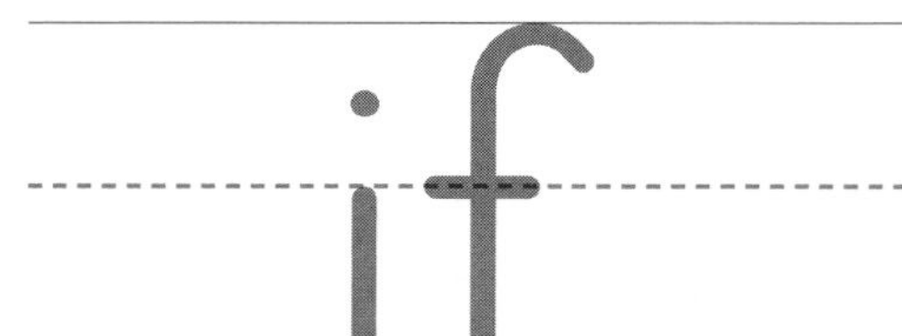

f i n

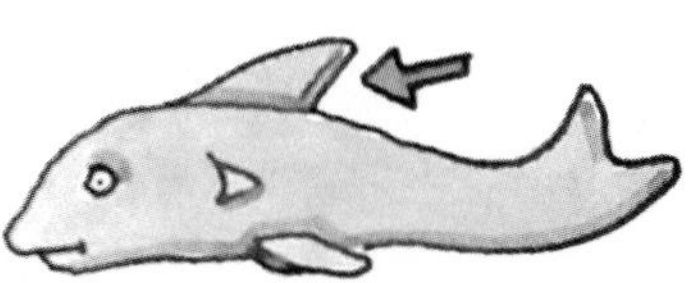

f i t

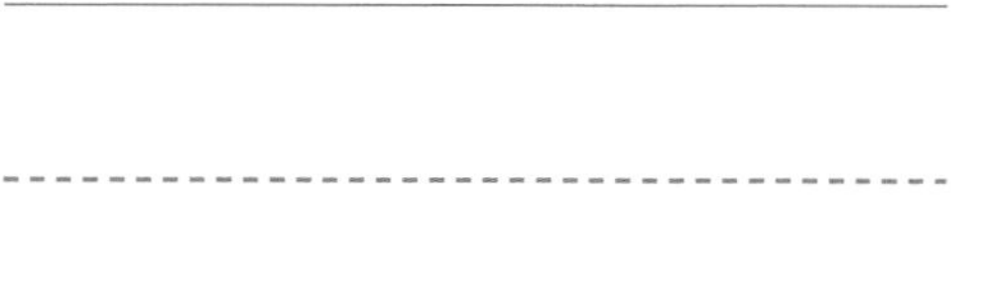

f a n

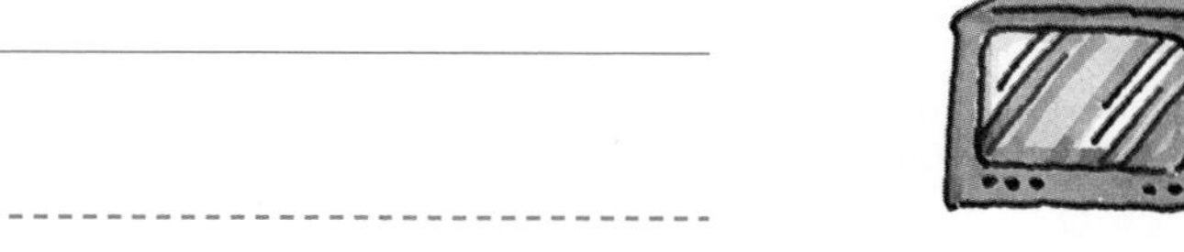

Blend the sounds and say the word. Write the word. Blend the sounds and say the word. Write the word. Draw a circle around the picture that goes with the word.

We fit!

We Fit!

We have a cat.

Dad can fit.

Mom can fit.

The cat can fit.

Tim can fit.

Nan can fit.

Name

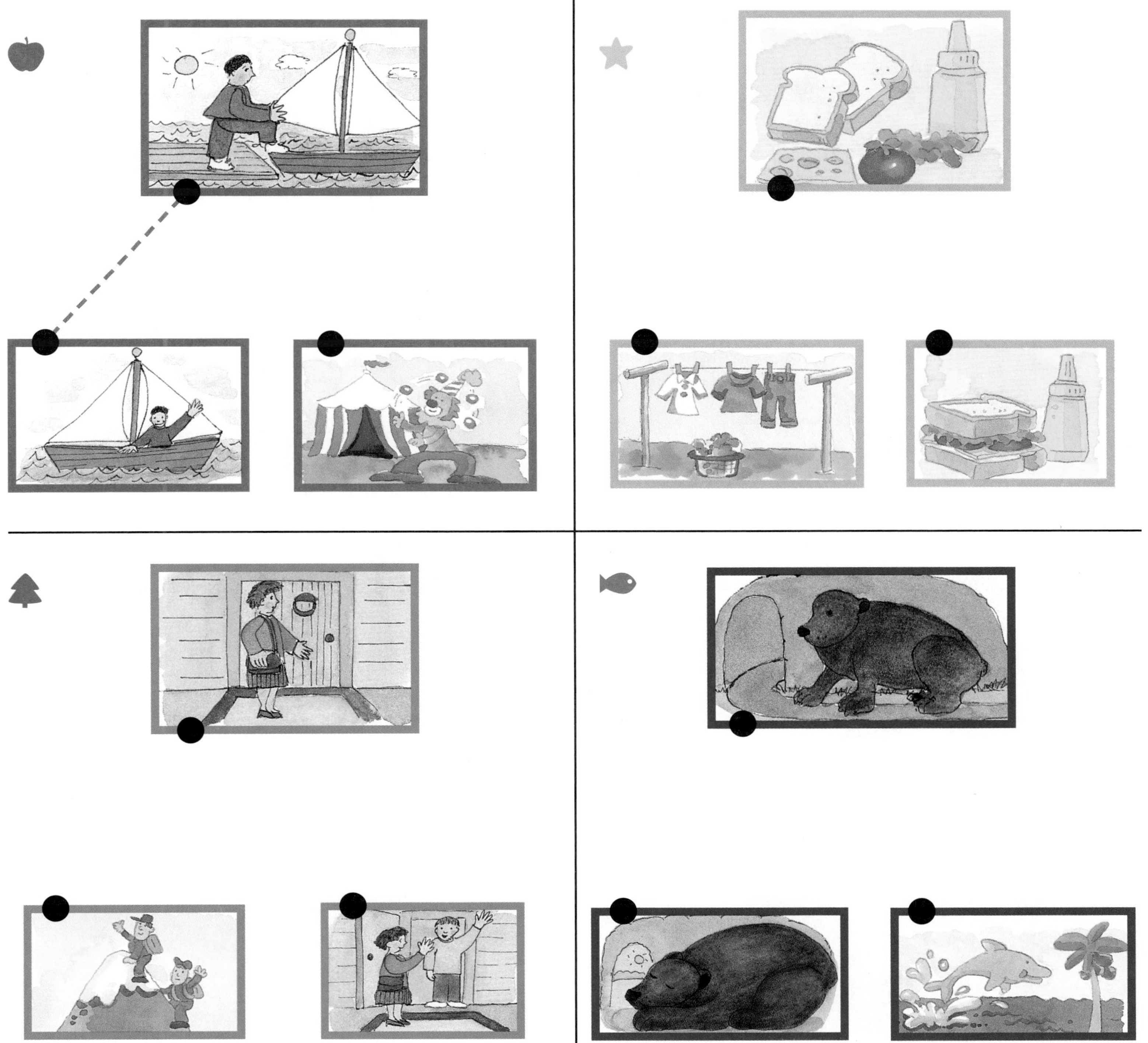

Look at each big picture. Draw a line to the small picture that shows what will happen next.

Name ______________________________

fin fan

fan

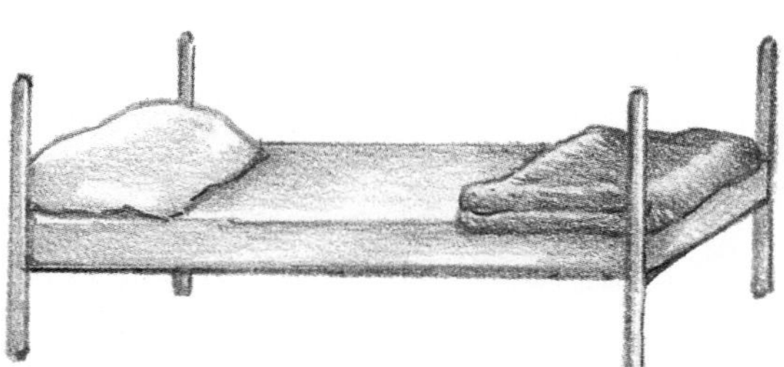

dot cot

sit can

mat cat

Draw a circle around the word that names the picture. • Say the word. • Then write the word.

Name ______________________________

We have a fat cat.

Tom is the fat cat.

Tim said, "You are my cat."

Read the sentences. Then do the following: Draw a circle around the word *have*. Draw a line under the word *we*. Draw a circle around the word *is*. Draw a circle around the word *you*. Draw a line under the word *are*.

Name________________________

c

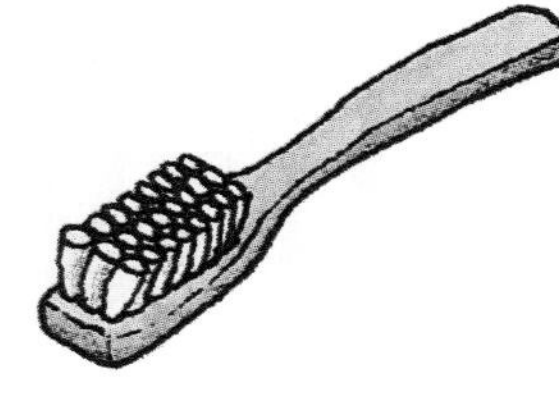

Say the name of each picture. • Under the picture write the letter for the sound you hear at the beginning of the picture name.

Name ______________________________

Draw a circle around the animal that is light. Draw a line under the item that is tall. Cross out the window that is high. Draw a circle around the person who is on top. Draw a line under the person who is on the bottom. Draw a box around the person who is in the middle.

Name________________________

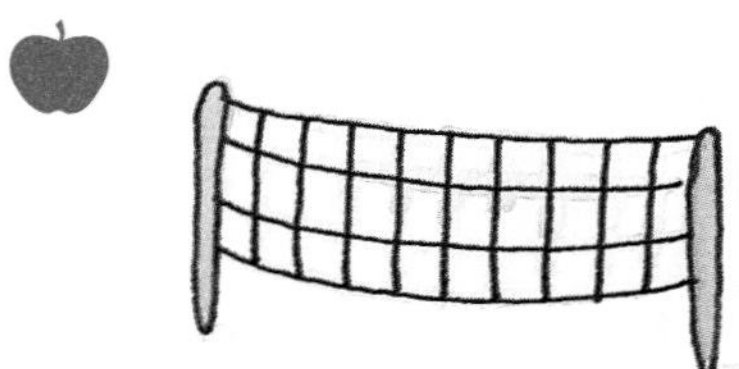

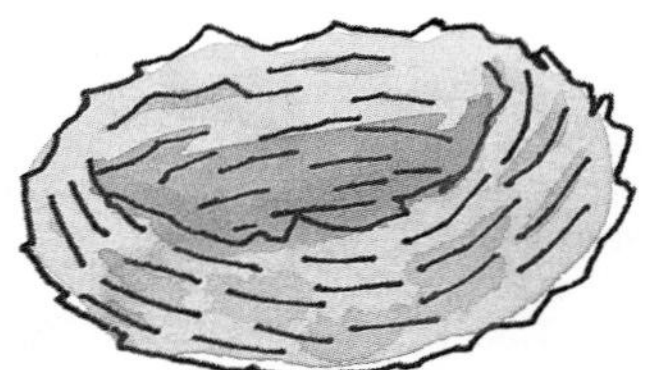
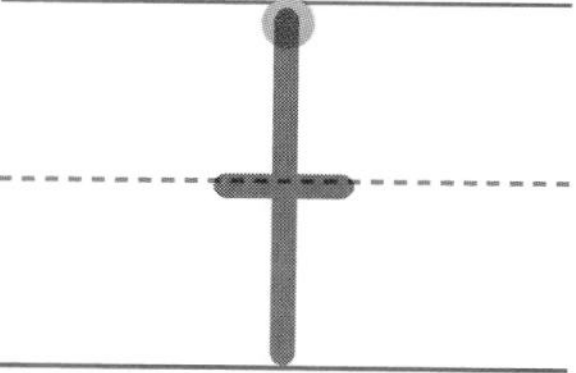

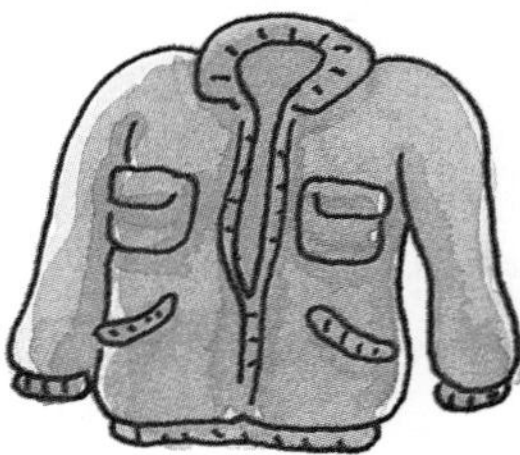

Write the letter *t.* • Then say each picture name. • Draw a circle around each picture that has the same ending sound as *pot.*

Name ______________________________

Look at the picture. • Find 3 things that are make-believe. • Circle them.

Name ____________________

t

f

c

t

Trace the letter. Say the word that names the picture. Write the letter in the correct box to show if you hear the sound /t/, /k/, or /f/ at the beginning, the middle, or the end of the word.

Name________________________________

we have you have

have you we are

you we are have

you have are we

Read the words. Draw a circle around the word *we*. Draw a circle around the word *are*. Draw a circle around the word *you*. Draw a circle around the word *have*.

Name

d o t

dot

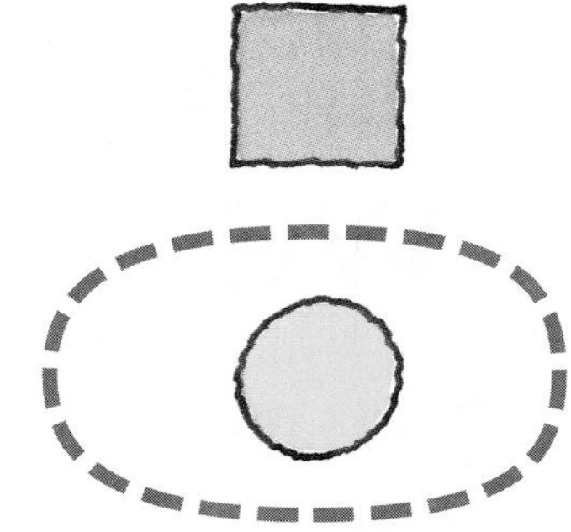

c o t

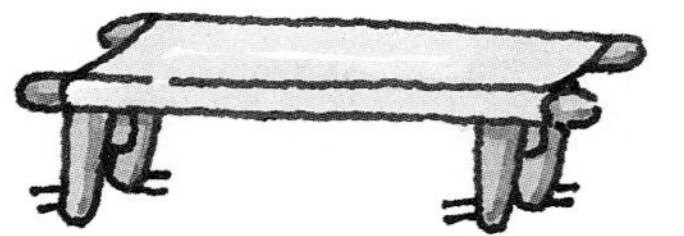

M o m

T o m

Blend the sounds and say the word. • Write the word. • Draw a circle around the picture that goes with the word.

It is a fat cat!

A Tin Can

My dot is on the .

I have a tin can.

We sit on my tan mat.

Is it a cat?

We have a ◯.

The ◯ is on the tin can.

Name____

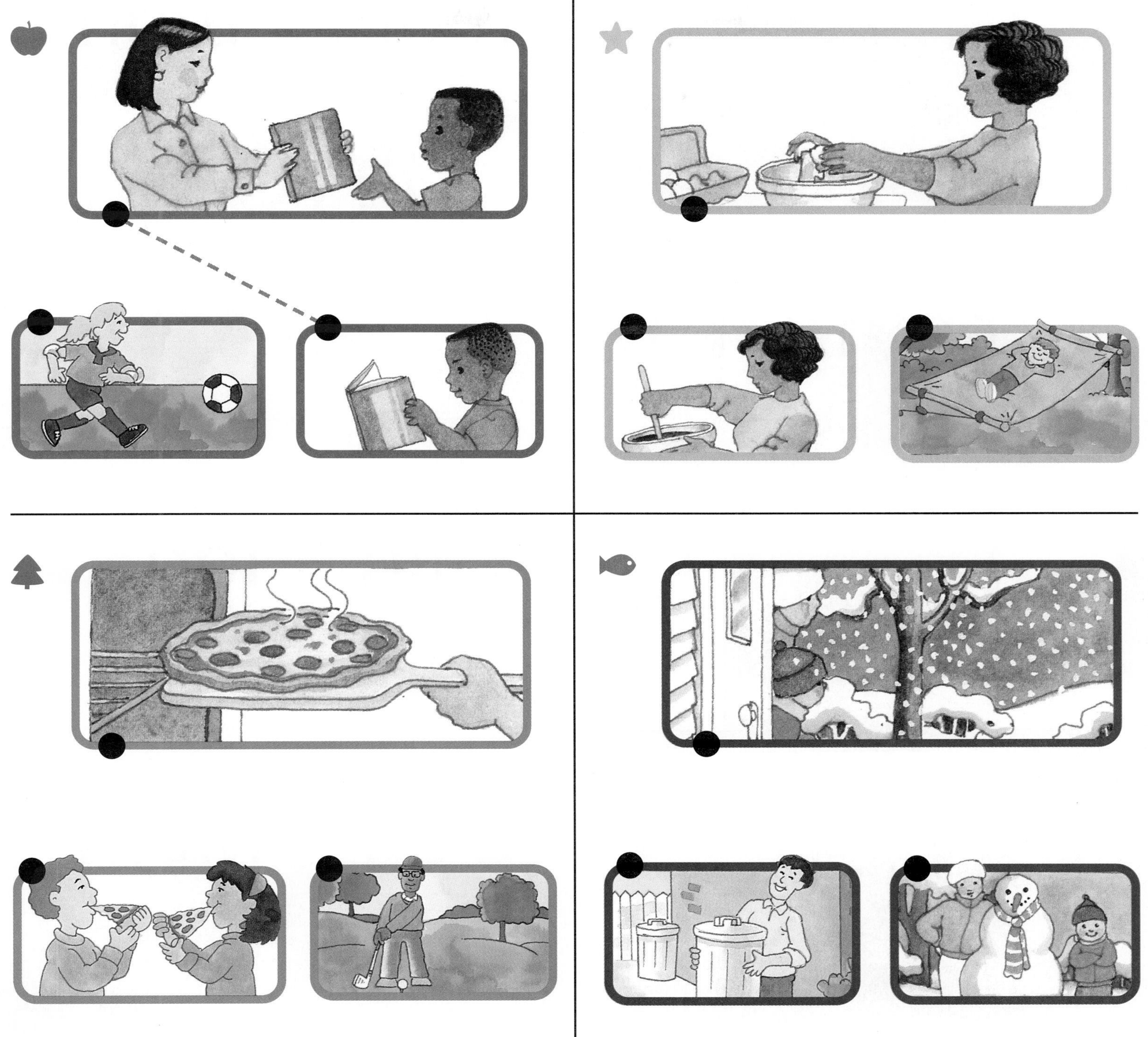

Look at each big picture. Draw a line to the small picture that shows what will happen next.

Name ____________________

mat man

mat

sit dot

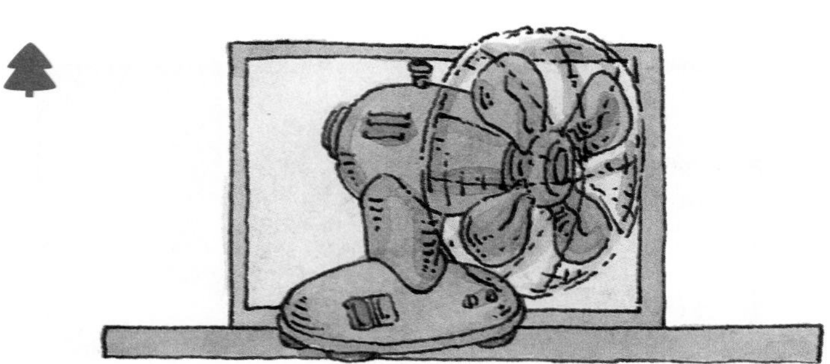

fin fan

Don Mom

Draw a circle around the word that names the picture. • Say the word. • Then write the word.

Name_______________

you	are	you	is
have	the	a	have
we	we	are	my
are	are	you	that

Say the first word in the row. • Draw a circle around the word where you see it in the same row.

Rr

Name ______________________

1. 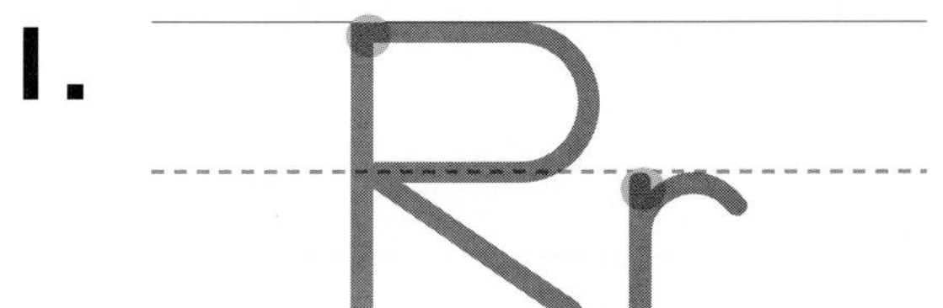

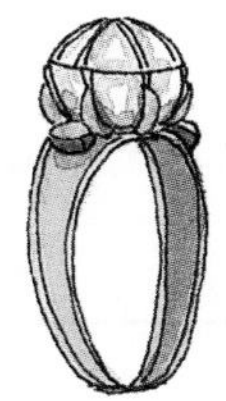 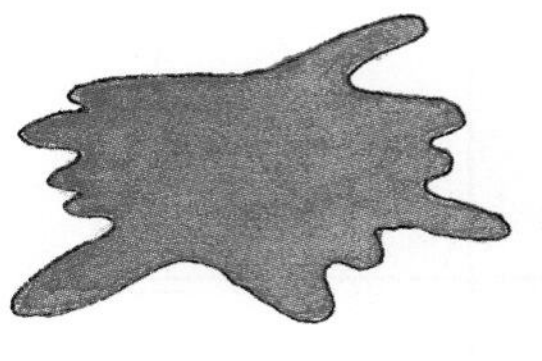 

2. 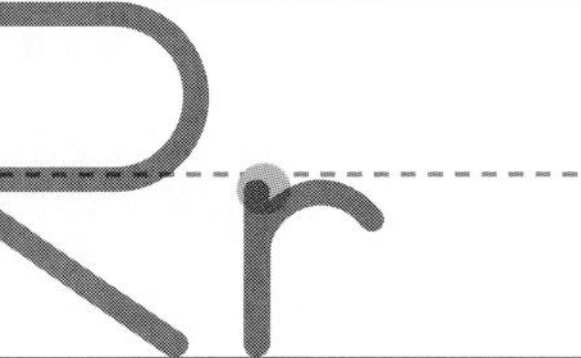

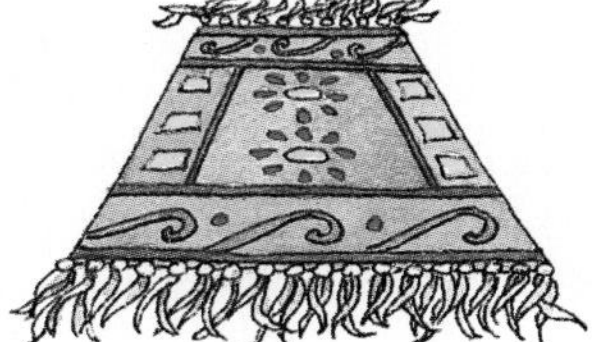  

3.

 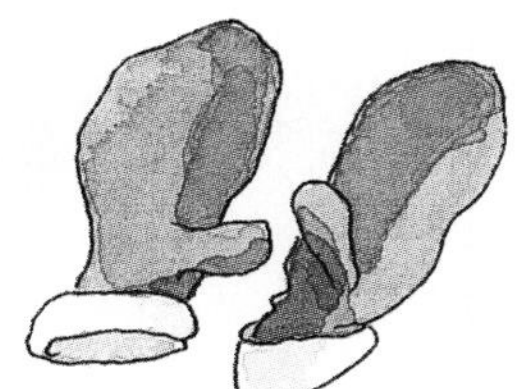 

4.

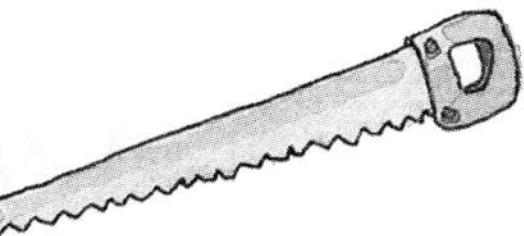 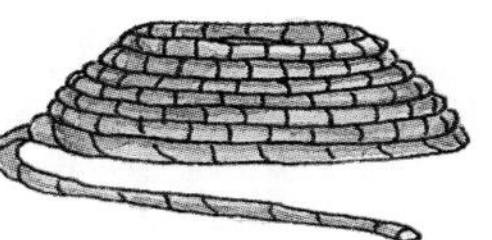 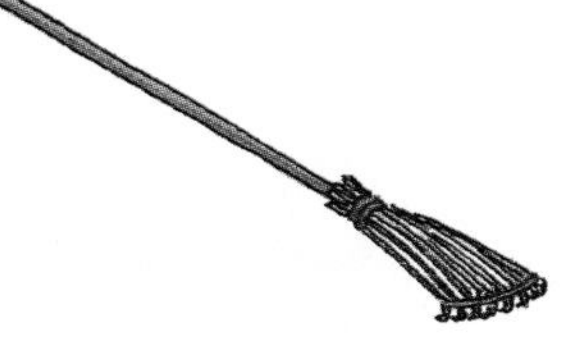

Write the letters *Rr.* • Say the word that names each picture. • Listen for the sound at the beginning of each word. • Circle each picture whose name begins with the same sound as *rainbow*.

Name ______________________

1.

2.

3.

4.

Draw a circle around the picture that shows something that is on. • Draw a line under the picture that shows something that is off.

Name ______________________________

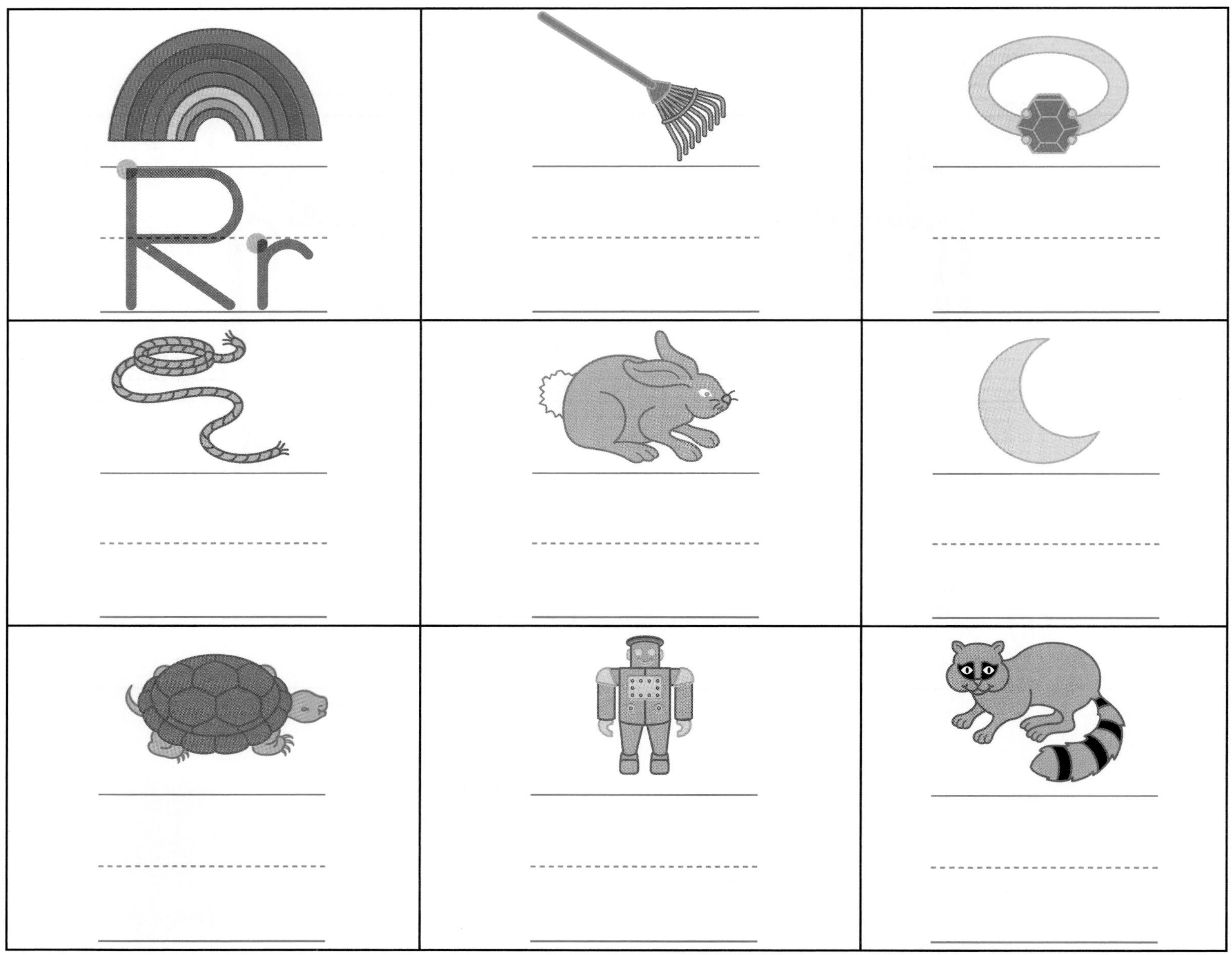

Say the word that names the picture. If the word begins with the /r/ sound, write the letters *Rr* on the line.

Name ______________________________

1.

The cat sat on a mat.

The cat ran to Mom.

2.

Nan is mad.

Sam is sad.

Look at each picture. • Then read the sentences. • Draw a line under the sentence that tells what the picture is all about.

Name______________________________

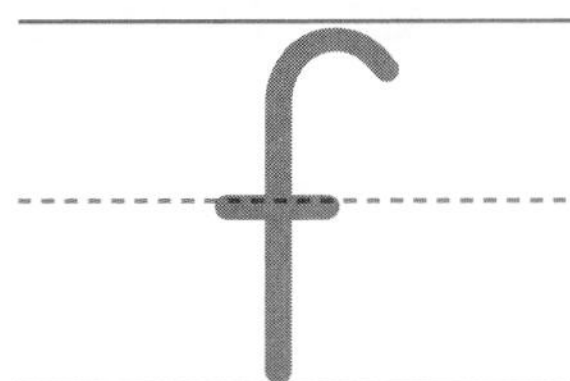

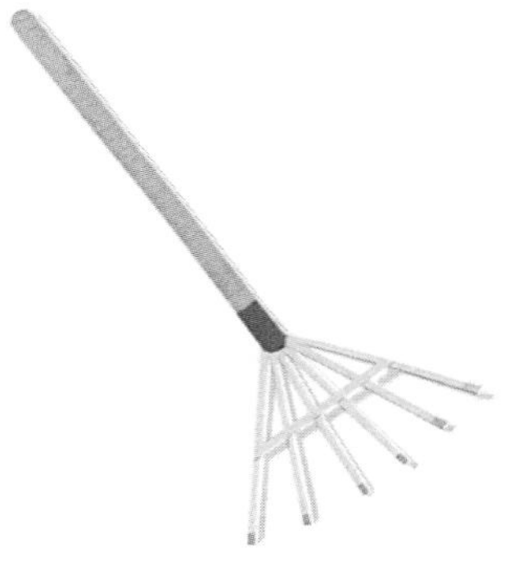

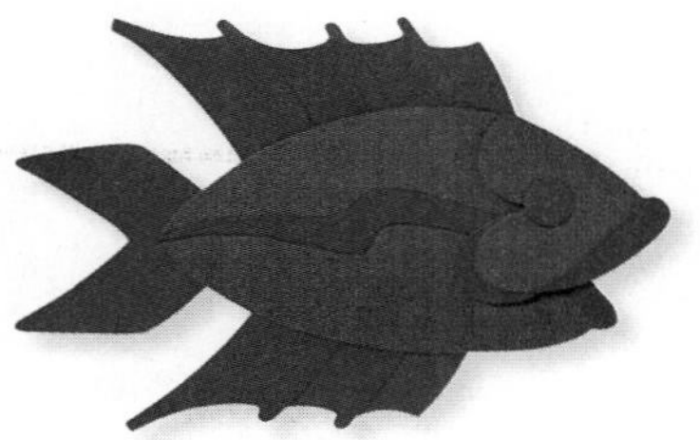

Say the name of each picture. • Then write the letter for the sound you hear at the beginning of the picture name.

Name________________________________

to

1. Nan ran to Dad.

2. Dad ran to Ron.

3. Ron ran to Mom.

4. Mom ran to Min.

Read the sentence. • Draw a line under the word *to* in the sentence.

Name ______________________________

1. r a t

rat

2. r o d

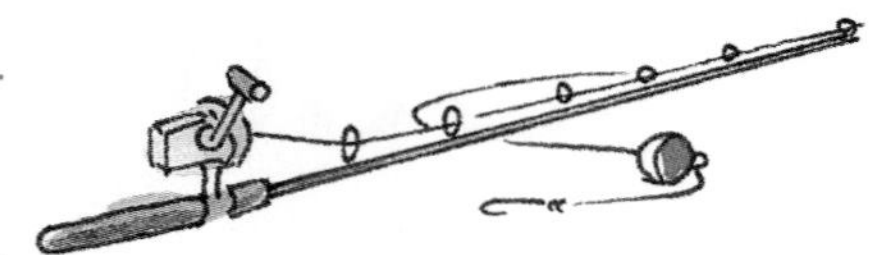

3. r a n

4. T i m

Blend the sounds and write the word. Say the word that names the picture.

You Are IT!

"You are IT!" said Ron.

Nan ran to Dad.

Ron, Tom, and Nan ran.

Ron ran to Tom.

"You are IT!" said Nan.

Tom ran to Nan.

"You are IT!" said Tom.

Name ______________________________

1.

A cat is on the cot.

Ron and Nan sat on the cot.

2.

Ron ran to Dad and Nan.

Mom and Dad sat.

Look at each picture. • Then read the sentences. • Draw a line under the sentence that tells what the picture is all about.

Name ______________________________

1. 

cat mat

cat

2. 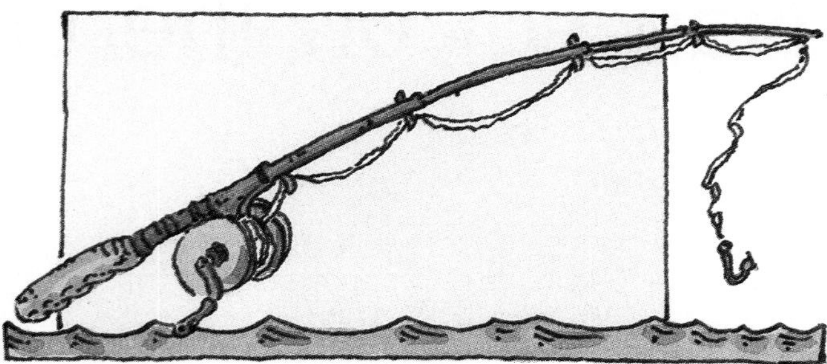

ran rod

3. 

Mom Dad

4. 

fin fan

Draw a circle around the word that names the picture. • Say the word. • Then write the word.

Name ____________________

1\.

The tot ran to Dad.

2\.

Is that the cat?

3\.

The cat ran to Mom.

4\.

That cat is Tom.

Read the sentences. **1.** Draw a circle around the word *to*. **2.** Draw a circle around the word *that*. **3.** Draw a circle around the word *the*. **4.** Draw a circle around the word *that*.

Pp

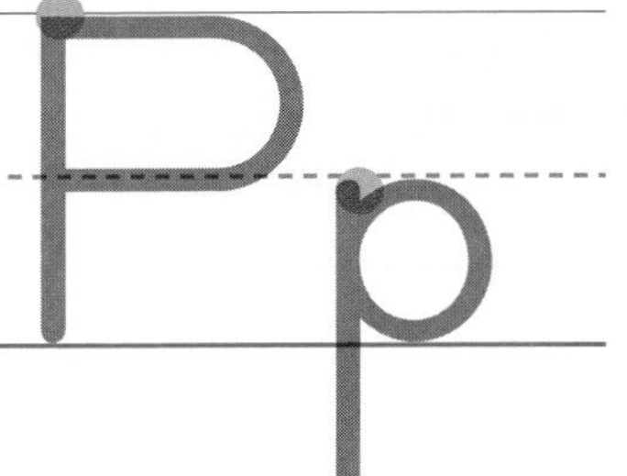

Name________________________________

1.

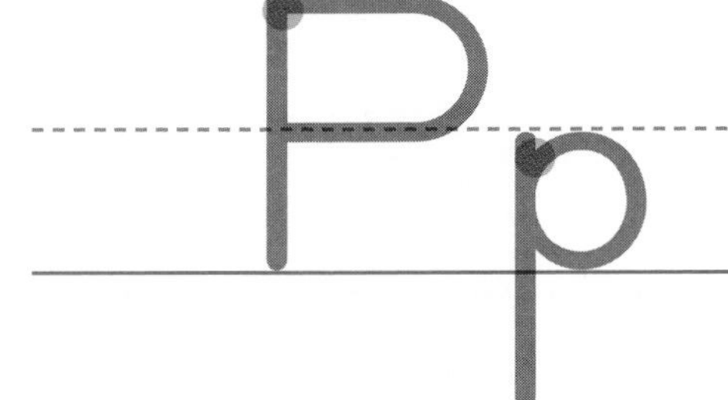

2.

3.

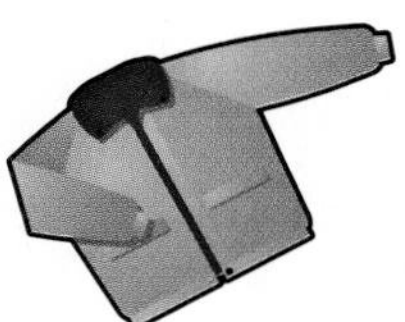

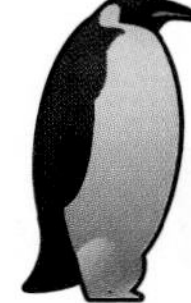

4.

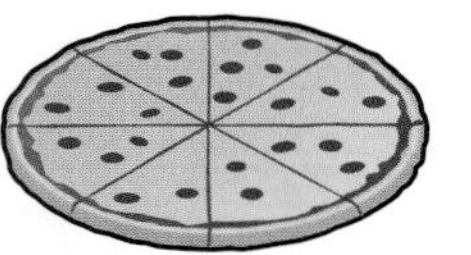

Write the letters *Pp.* • Say the word that names each picture. • Listen for the sound at the beginning of each word. • Circle each picture whose name begins with the same sound as *pig.*

Name ______________________________

1. Draw a circle around the worm that is inside the apple. **2.** Draw a circle around the bird that is outside the nest. **3.** Draw a circle around the cat that is outside the box. **4.** Draw a circle around the dog that is inside the doghouse.

_p

Name ____________________

1.

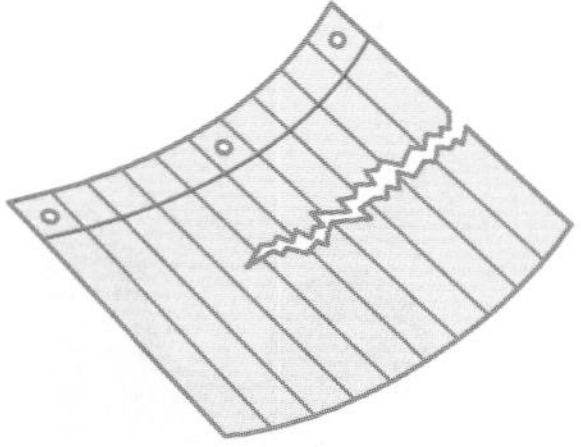

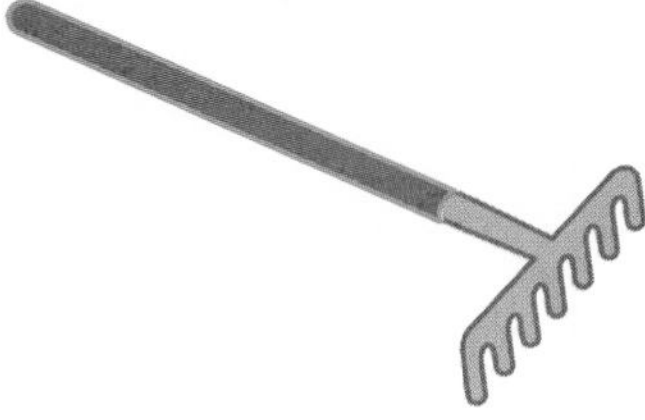

p

2.

3.

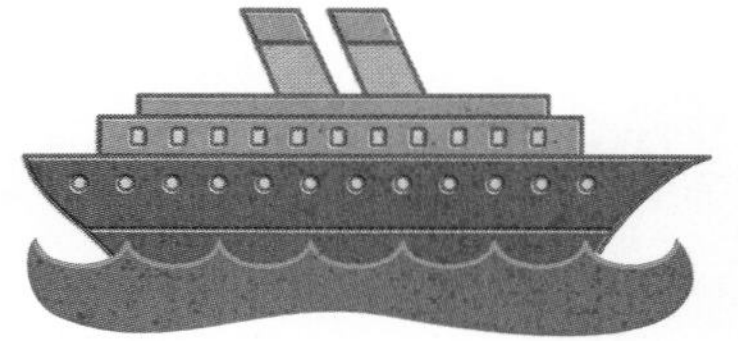

4.

Say the name of each picture. • Circle the pictures whose names have the same ending sound as *cap*. • Write the letter *p*.

Name ______________________________

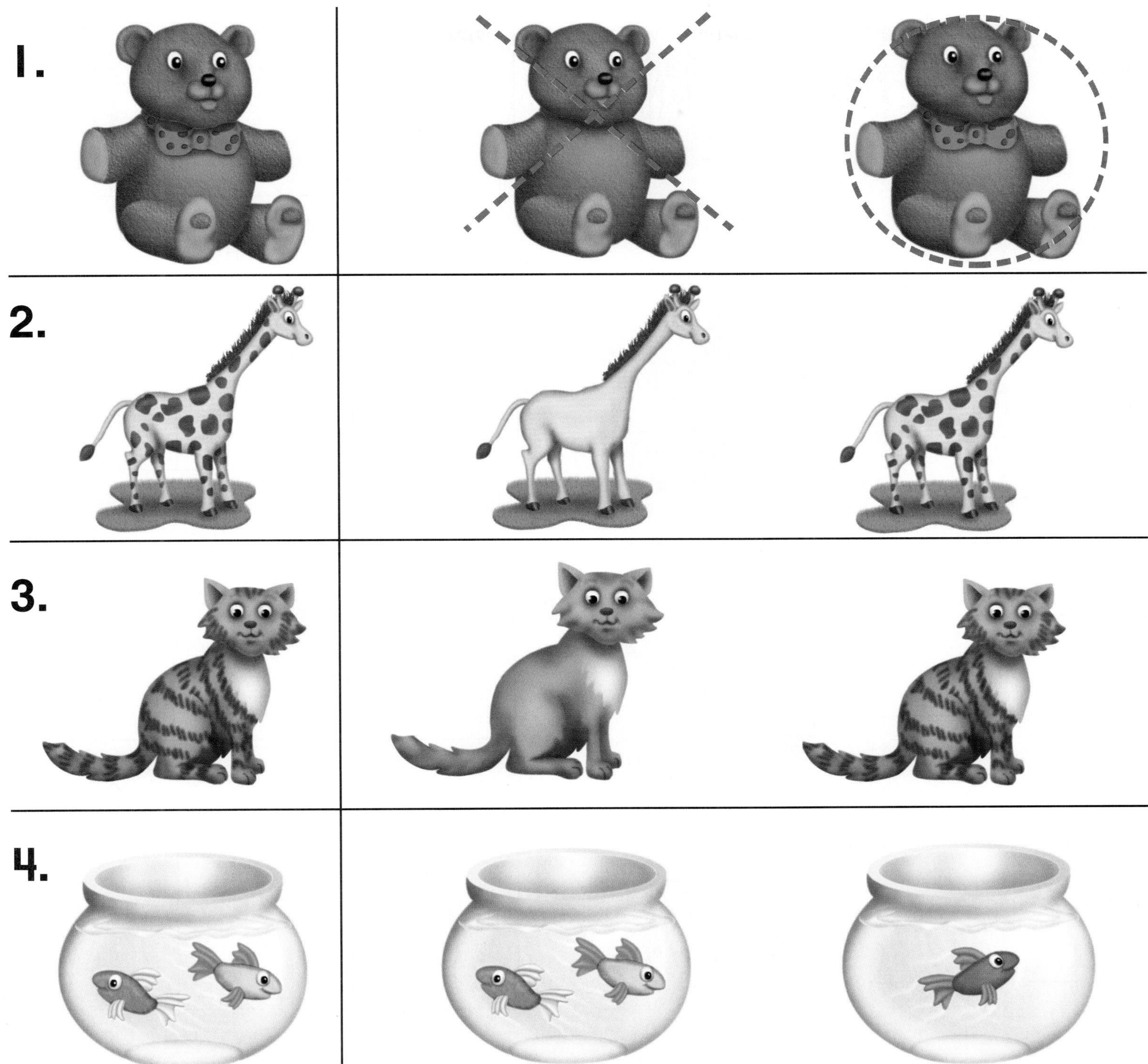

Look at the pictures in each row. Draw a circle around the picture that is the same as the picture on the left. Draw an X through the picture that is different.

Name

Trace the letter. Say the word that names the picture. Write the letter in the correct box to show if you hear the sound /p/ at the beginning, middle, or the end of the word.

Name____

me

1. Pam ran to me.

2. Ron ran to me.

3. My cat ran to me.

4. My cat sat on me!

Read the sentence. • Draw a line under the word *me* in the sentence.

Name ____________________

1. p a n

pan

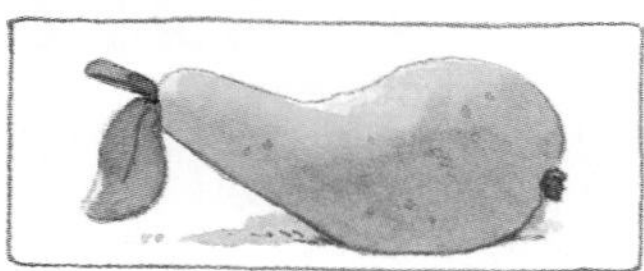

2. p i n

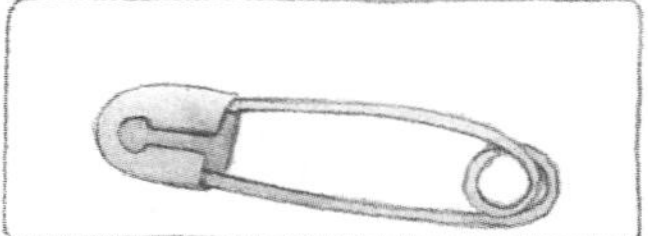

3. m o p

4. c a p

Blend the sounds and say the word. • Write the word. • Draw a circle around the picture that goes with the word.

It is Min!

8

Is It You?

Is it Ron?

6

"It is me," said Pam.

3

Is it Pam?

2

"It is not me!" said Ron.

7

Is it Pat?

4

"It is me," said Pat.

5

McGraw-Hill School Division

Name

Look at the pictures in each row. Draw a circle around the picture that is the same as the picture on the left. Draw an X through the picture that is different.

Name ____________________

1. 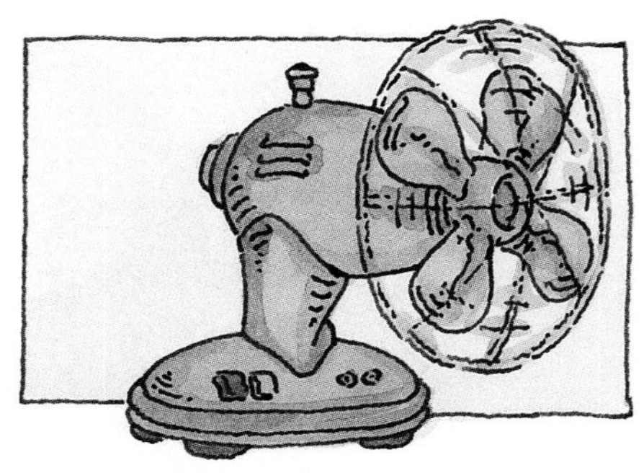

fan fin

fan

2. 

pot pin

3. 

cat can

4. 

top tin

Draw a circle around the word that names the picture. • Say the word. • Then write the word.

Name

1.

The cat ran to you.

2.

The cat ran to me.

3.

The cat sat on me.

Read the sentences. Then do the following: **1.** Draw a circle around the word *you*. **2.** Draw a circle around the word *to*. **3.** Draw a circle around the word *me*.

Ll

Name____________________

1. Ll

2. 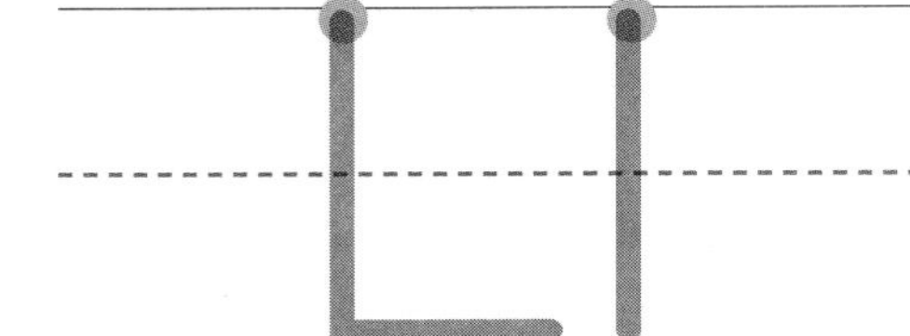

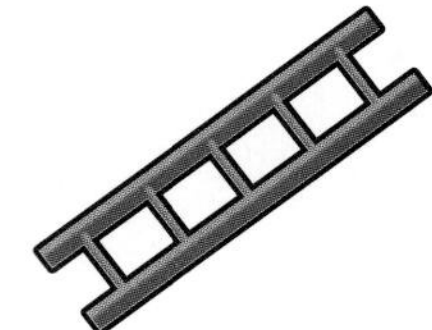

3.

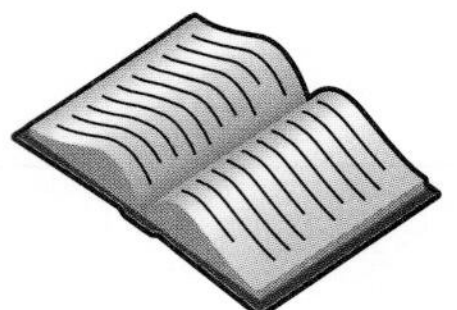

4.

Write the letters *Ll*. • Say the word that names each picture. • Listen for the sound at the beginning of each word. • Draw a circle around each picture whose name begins with the same sound as *lamb*.

Name____

1.

2.

3.

4.

1. Draw a ball under the table. **2.** Draw a bird under the cloud.
3. Draw a bridge over the water. **4.** Draw a kite over the tree.

Name ____________________

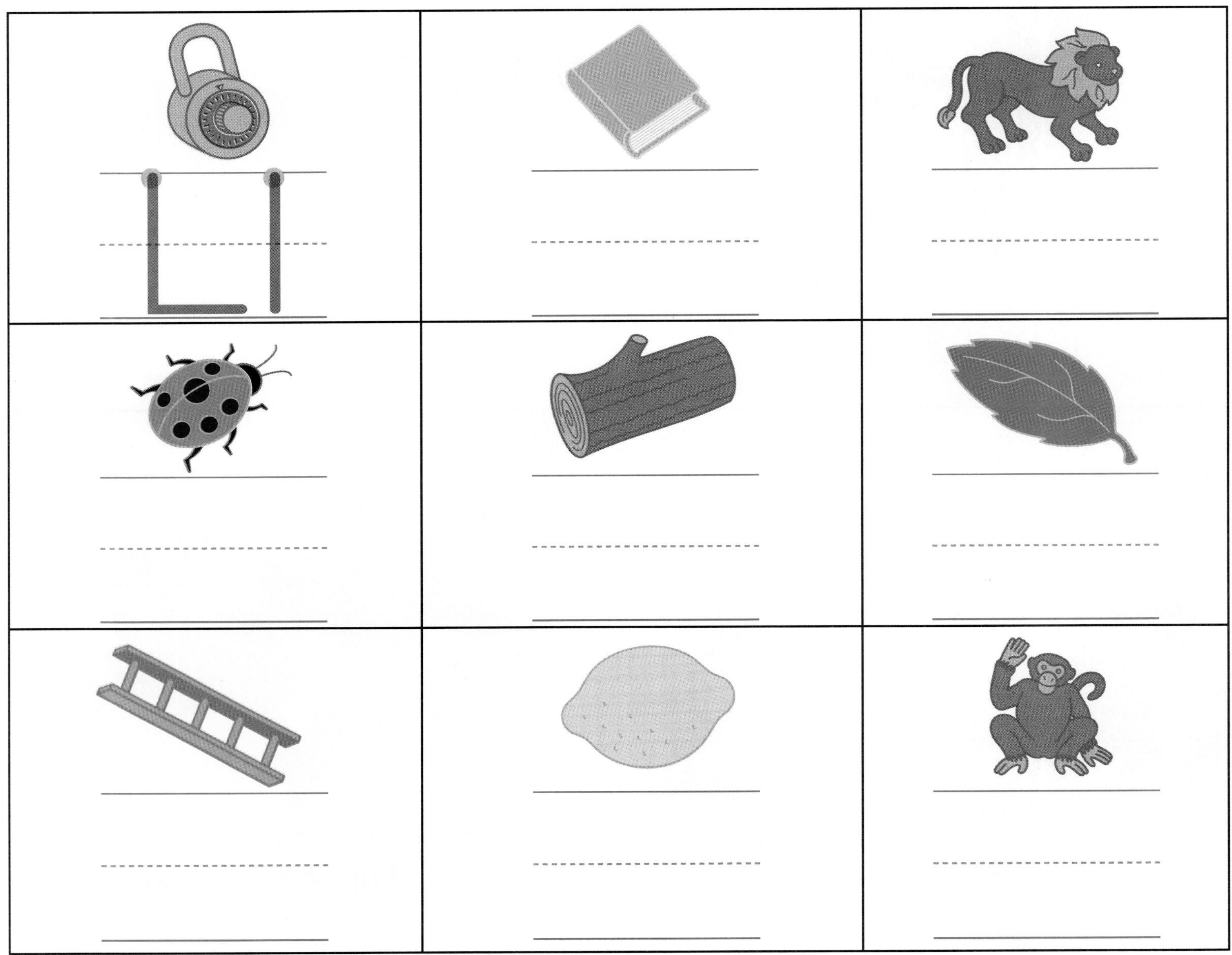

Say the word that names the picture. If the word begins with the /l/ sound, write the letters *Ll* on the line.

Name ____________________

1.

Dan can pat the cat.

Pam can pat the cat.

2.

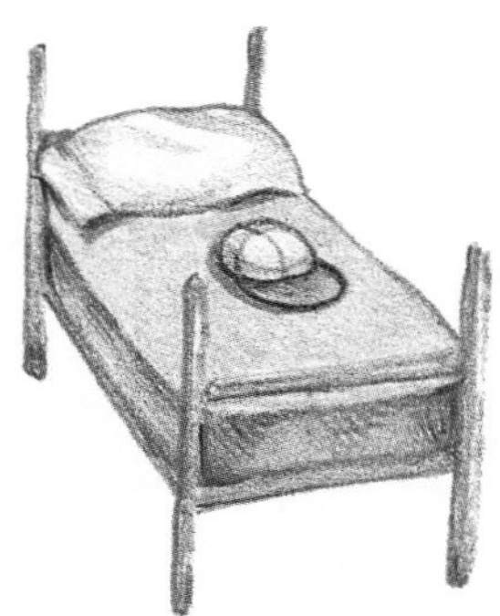

The cap is on the cot.

Ron is on the cot.

3.

The pan and the pot are tan.

The can is on the pan.

Look at each picture. • Then read the sentences. • Draw a line under the sentence that tells what the picture is all about.

Name

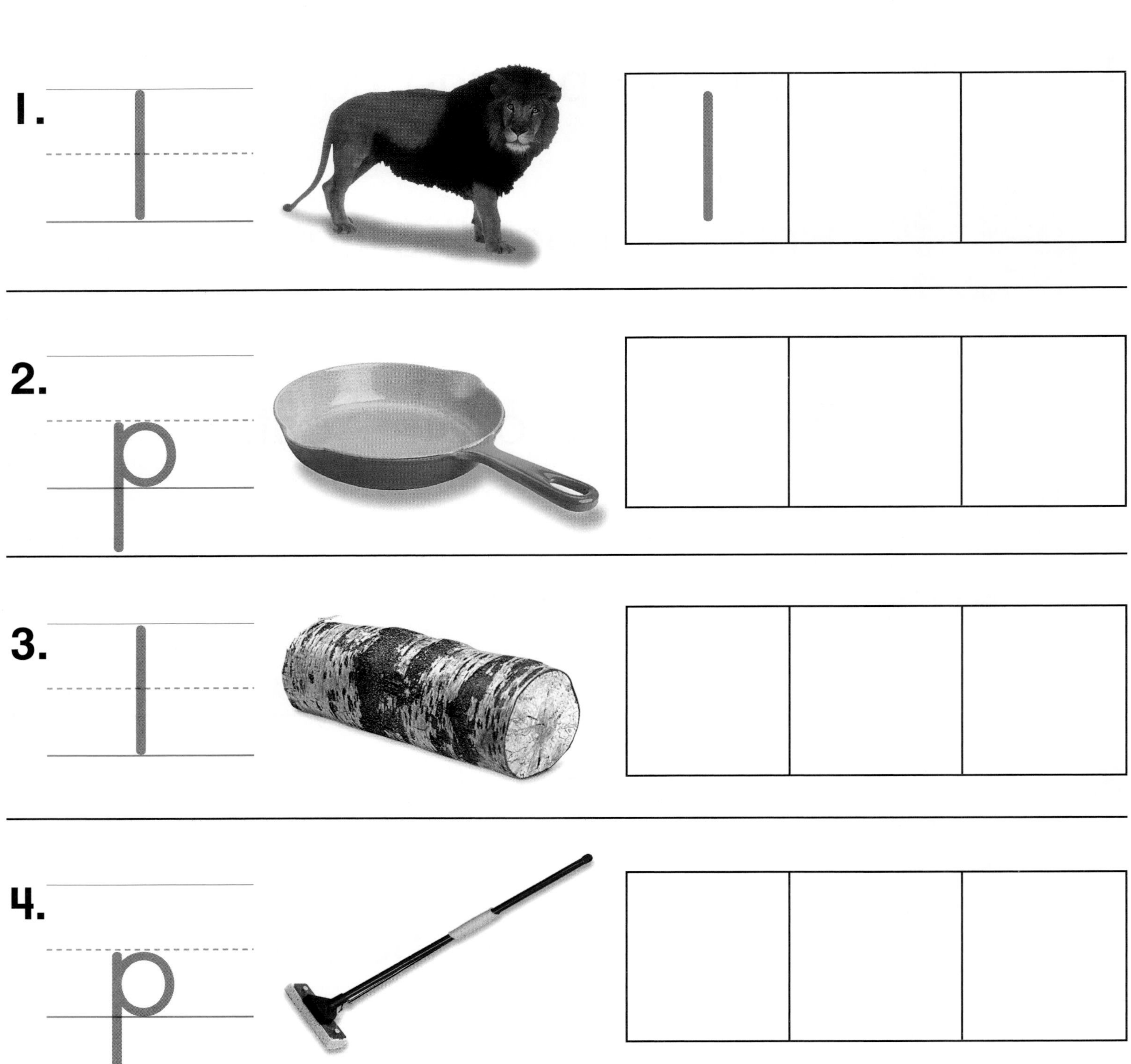

Trace the letter. Say the word that names the picture. Write the letter in the correct box to show if you hear the sound /l/ or /p/ at the beginning, middle, or the end of the word.

Name ____________________

go

1.

"Go to the cot," I said.

2.

The cat can go to the cot.

3.

I can go to the cot.

4.

We can go and nap.

Read the sentence. • Draw a line under the word *go* in the sentence.

Name ____________________

1. l i d — lid

2. l a p

3. l i p

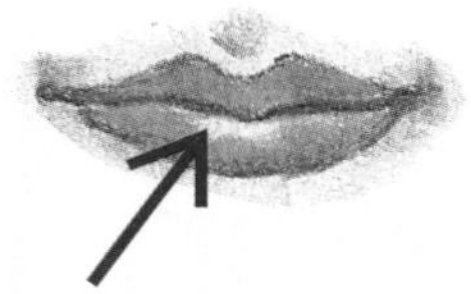

4. l i t

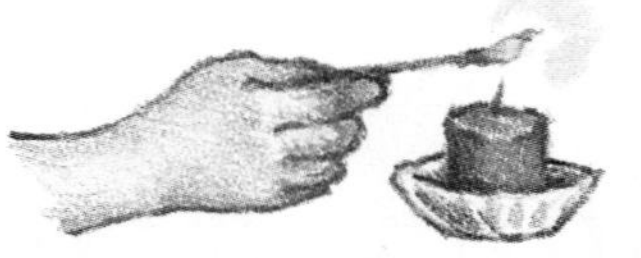

Blend the sounds and write the word. Say the word that names the picture.

Lad can nap!

Go, Lad, Go

Can you go to the mat?

Lad can go to the 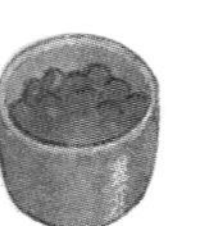 .

Can you go to the  ?

Lad can go to my lap.

Can you sit?

Lad can sit.

Name____

1. Nan can sit on the cot.

Tim and the cat have a nap.

---

2. 

Pam can fit the lid on the pot.

"I have a mop," said Pam.

---

3. 

"Sit on my lap," said Mom.

"Pat the cat," said Dad.

Look at each picture. • Then read the sentences. • Draw a line under the sentence that tells what the picture is all about.

Name ________________________________

1.

sad sit

sad

2.

rod rat

3.

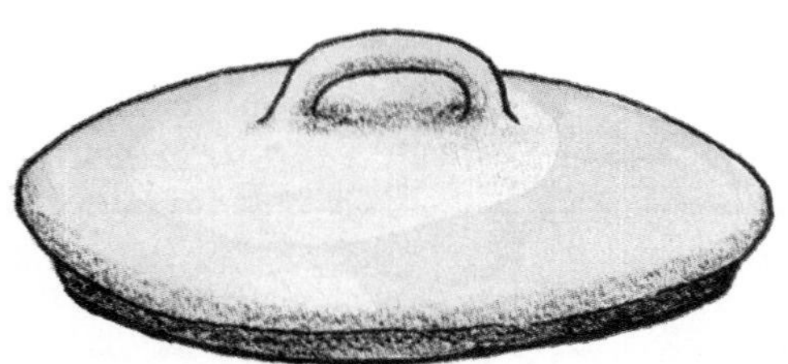

lad lid

4.

man mop

Draw a circle around the word that names the picture. • Say the word. • Then write the word.

Name

1.

"Go to the top," said Ron.

2.

"You can go," said Dad.

3.

"Go," Mom said to me.

Read the sentences. Then do the following: **1.** Draw a circle around the words *go* and *to.* **2.** Draw a circle around the word *you.* **3.** Draw a circle around the word *me.*

Uu

Name

1.

Uu

2.

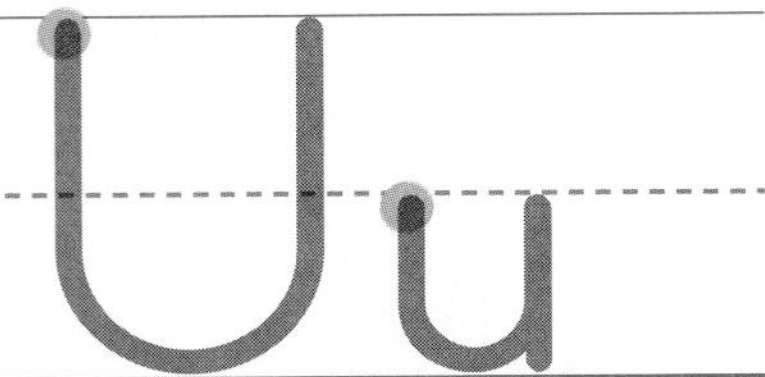

3.

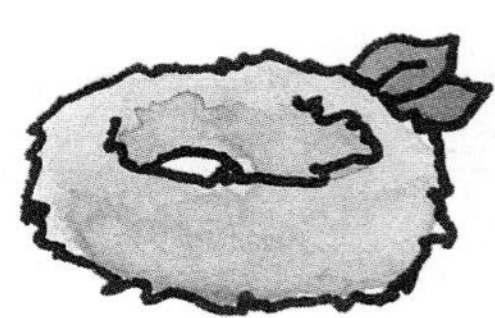

4.

Write the letters *Uu*. Say the word that names each picture. • Listen for the sound at the beginning of each word. • Draw a circle around each picture whose name begins with the same sound as *umbrella*.

Name ____________________

1.

2.

3.

4.

Draw a circle around the picture that shows up. • Draw a line under the picture that shows down.

_u_

Name______________________________

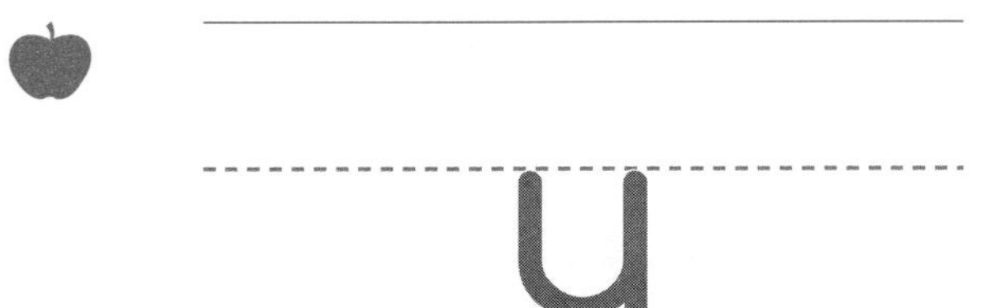
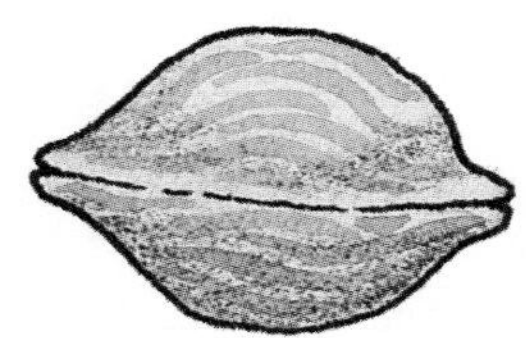

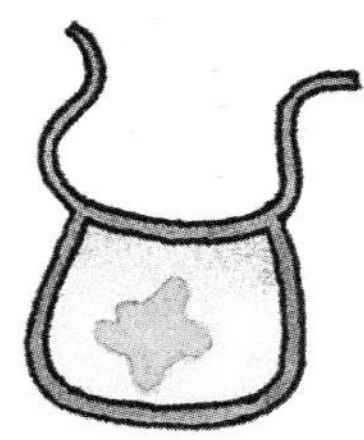

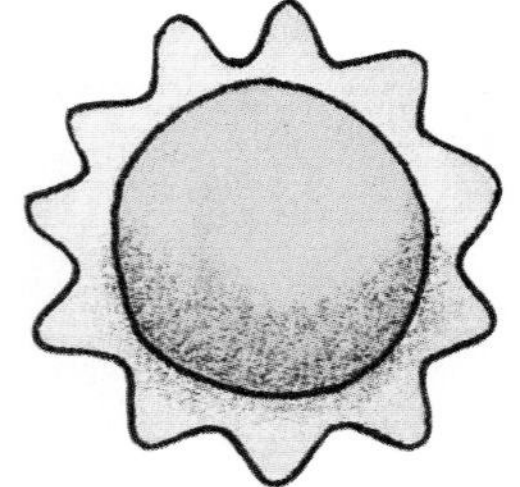

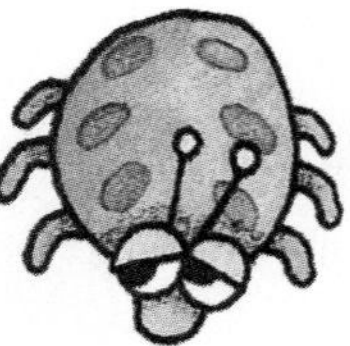
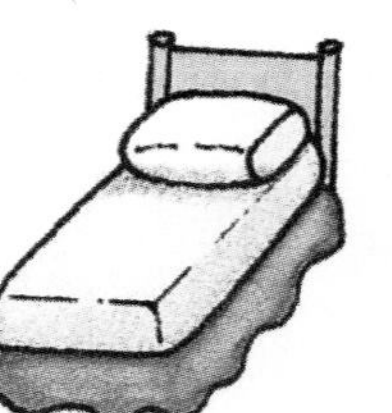

Write the letter *u*. • Say the word that names each picture. • Listen for the sound in the middle of each word. • Circle each picture whose name has the same middle sound as *sun*.

Name ____________________

Look at the two plants at the top of the page. • Then look at the pictures along the left side of the page. • Under each plant, put a ✔ on the line if the plant has that part. • Put an ✘ on the line if the plant does not have that part.

Name

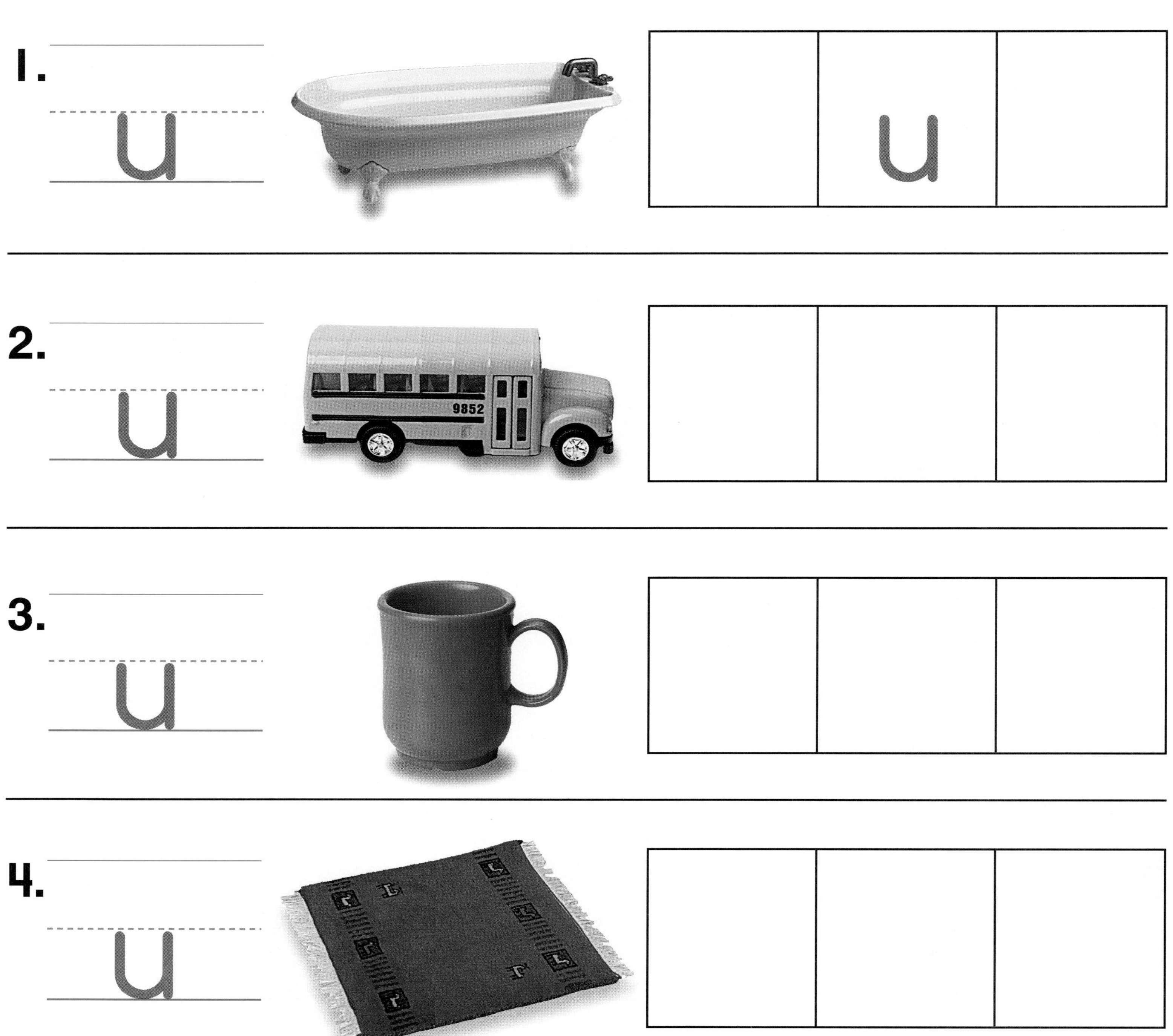

Trace the letter. Say the word that names the picture. Write the letter in the correct box to show if you hear the sound /u/*u* at the beginning, middle, or the end of the word.

Name ________________________________

do

1. Do you have a cat?

2. I do not have a cat.

3. Do you have a pup?

4. I do have a tan pup!

Read the sentence. • Draw a line under the word *do* in the sentence.

Name ______________________________

1. s u n

sun

2. 

3. n u t

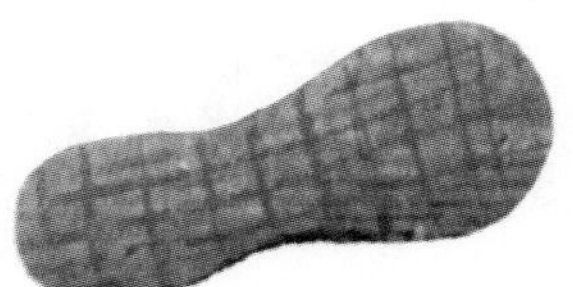

4. p u p

Blend the sounds and write the word. Say the word that names each picture.

Mud is fun, fun, fun!

Mud Fun

You sat in the mud!

You can have a pot, Pam.

Nan, do you have a pot?

2

I did sit in the mud.

7

Nan, do you have a cup?

4

You can have a cup, Pam.

5

Name ____________________

1.

2.

3.

Look at the two snails at the top of the page. • Then look at the pictures along the left side of the page. • Under each snail, put a ✔ on the line if the snail has that part. • Put an ✘ on the line if the snail does not have that part.

Name ____________________

1.

pop pup

pup

2.

pin pot

3.

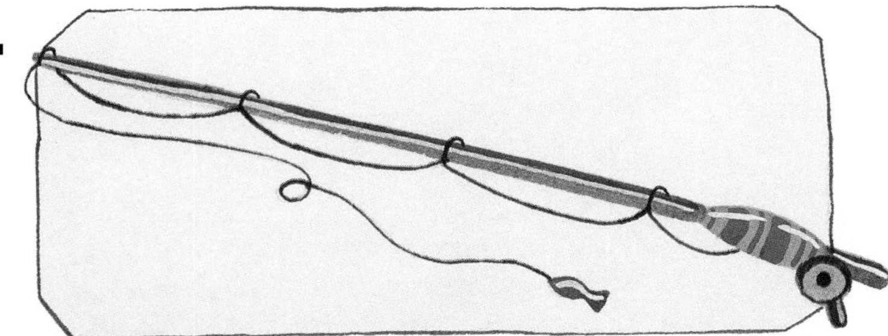

rod run

4.

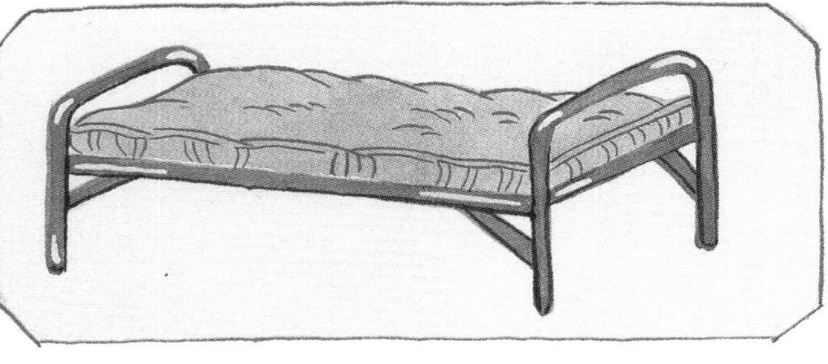

cut cot

Draw a circle around the word that names the picture. • Say the word. • Then write the word.

Name ______________________________

1.

Pam said to me, "Go sit!"

2.

I said, "I do have a mat."

3.

Pam and I do sit.

Read each sentence. 1. Draw a circle around the word *me*. Draw a line under the word *go*.
2. Draw a circle around the word *I* each time you see it. Draw a line under the word *do*.
3. Draw a circle around the word *do.* Draw a line under the word *and.*

Name______________________________

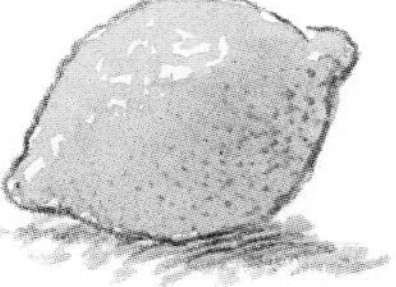

Say the name of each picture. • Then write the letter for the sound you hear at the beginning of the picture name.

Name ________________________________

1.

2.

3.

4.

1. Draw a circle around the person who is *on* the couch. Draw a line under the person who is *off* the couch. **2.** Draw a circle around the dog that is *inside*. Draw a line under the dog that is *outside*. **3.** Draw a circle around the bird that is *over* the tree. Draw a line under the bird that is *under* the tree. **4.** Draw a circle around the kite that is *up*. Draw a line under the kite that is *down*.

Name ______________________

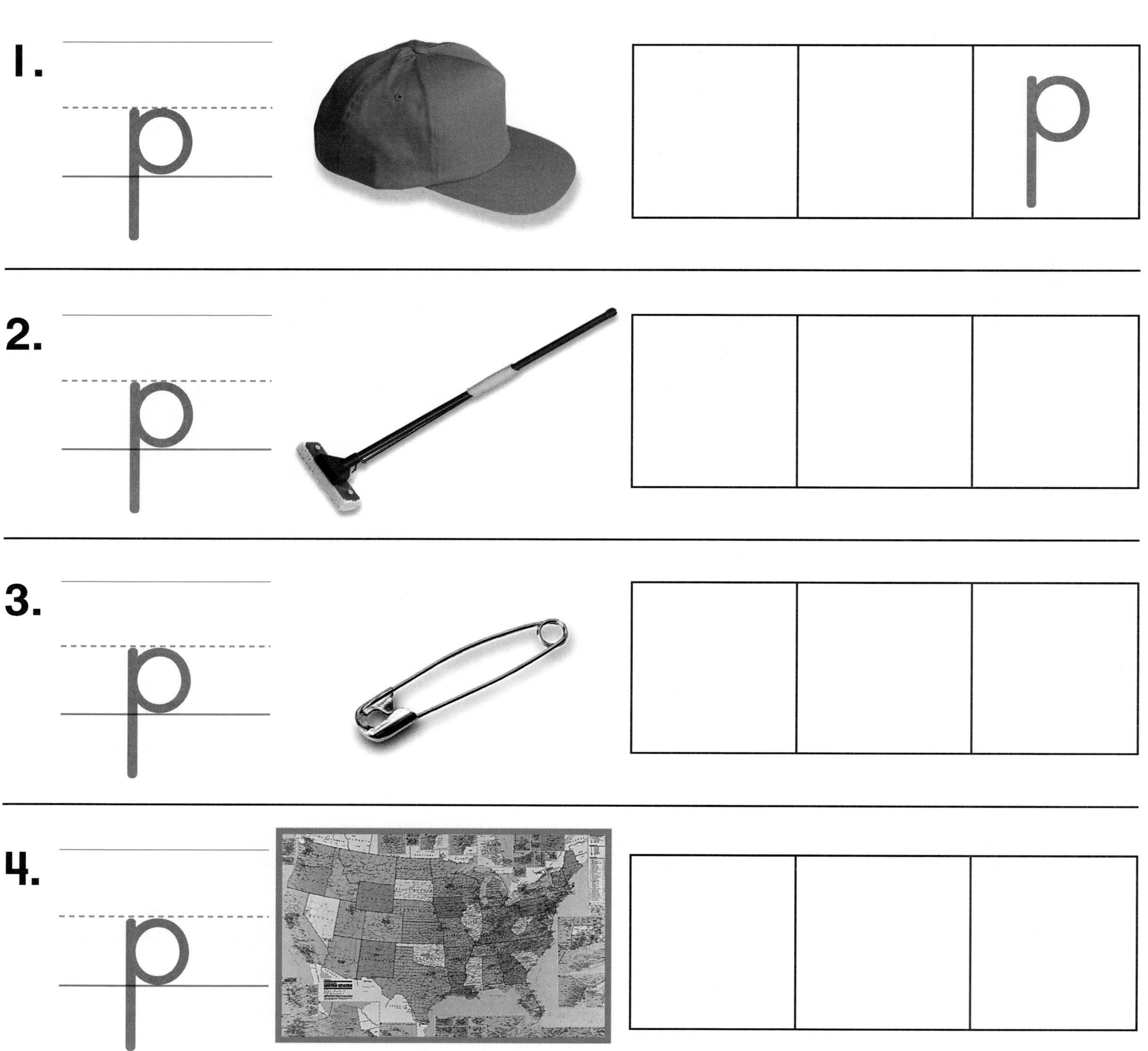

Trace the letter. Say the word that names the picture. Write the letter in the correct box to show if you hear the sound /p/ at the beginning, middle, or the end of the word.

McGraw-Hill School Division

Name ____________________

1. 

My cat ran to Dad.

My pup ran to Pam.

---

2. 

The cat can nap on the cot.

The pup is in the mud.

---

3. 

The pup can fit on the mat.

The pup can fit in the cap.

Look at each picture. • Then read the sentences. • Draw a line under the sentence that tells what the picture is all about.

Name ____________________

1. 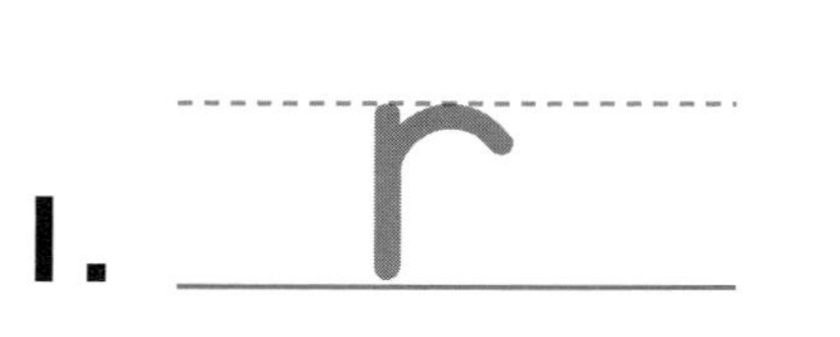

2. 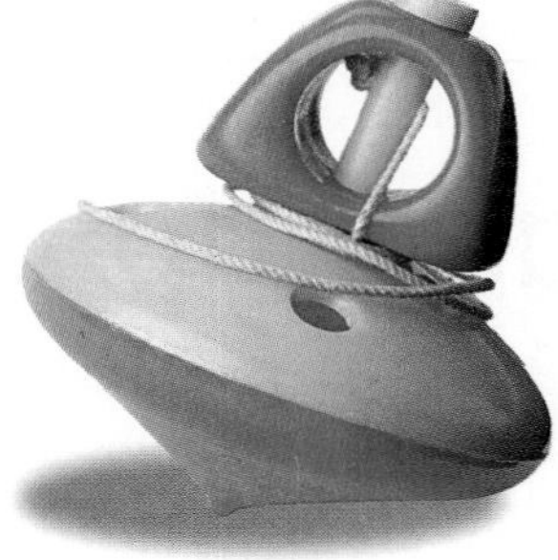
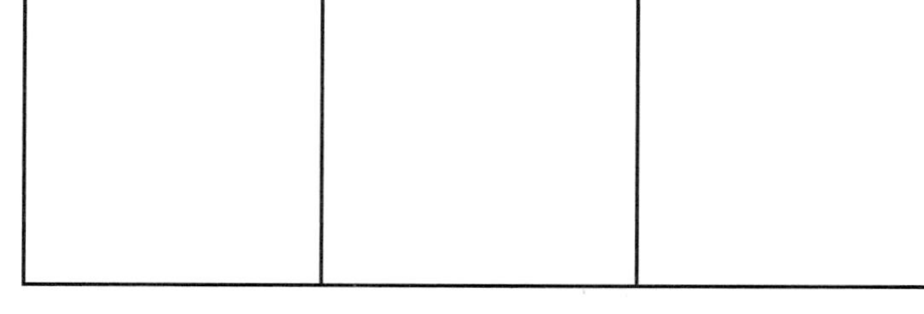

3. 

4. 
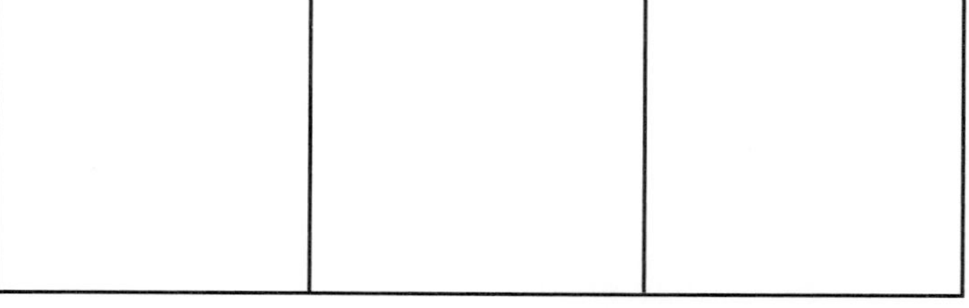

Trace the letter. Say the word that names the picture. Write the letter in the correct box to show if you hear the sound /r/*r*, /p/*p*, or /l/*l* at the beginning, middle, or the end of the word.

Name ______________________________

1. do that to my

2. me we is to

3. go you said me

4. have has for go

Read the words. **1.** Draw a circle around the word *do.* **2.** Draw a circle around the word *to.* **3.** Draw a circle around the word *me.* **4.** Draw a circle around the word *go.*

Name

1. s u n

sun

2. n u t

3. p u p

4. c u p

Blend the sounds and say the word. • Write the word. • Draw a circle around the picture that goes with the word.

We can mop, mop, mop!

Ron and Me

We can mop the mud!

Run to my lap, Ron.

Ron is my pup.

Mop the mud, Ron.

We have fun in the mud!

Go to the mop, Ron.

Name________________________________

1.

2.

3.

Look at the two bicycles at the top of the page. • Then look at the pictures along the left side of the page. • Under each bicycle, put a ✔ on the line if the bicycle has that part. • Put an ✘ on the line if the bicycle does not have that part.

Name

1. 

fin fan

fin

2. 

Mom mud

3. 

rip run

4. 

dot dig

Draw a circle around the word that names the picture. • Say the word. • Then write the word.

Name ______________________________

1. go	my do go to
2. me	we go my me
3. to	to do the is
4. do	I a to do

Say the first word in the row. • Draw a circle around the word where you see it in the same row.

Kk

Name__________________________________

1. 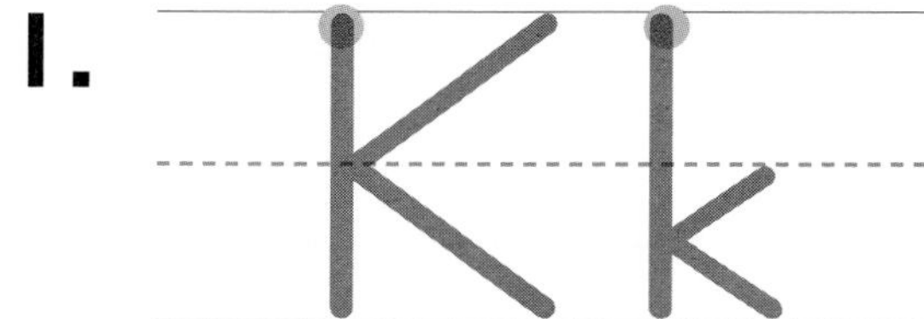

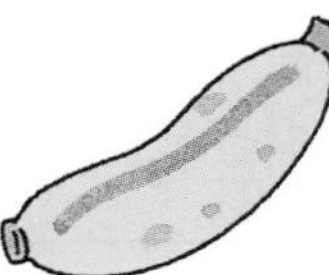

2. 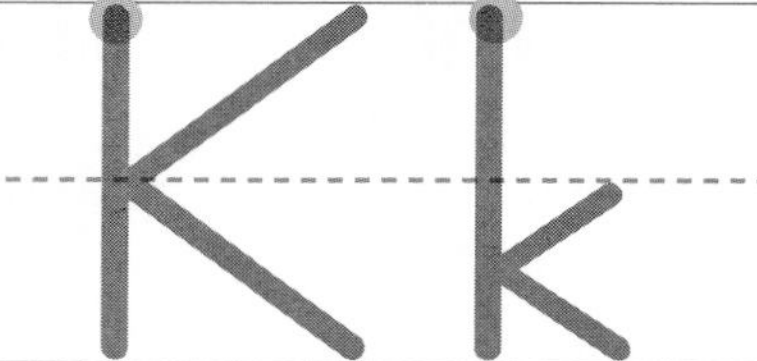

3.

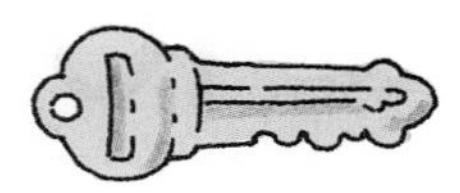

4.

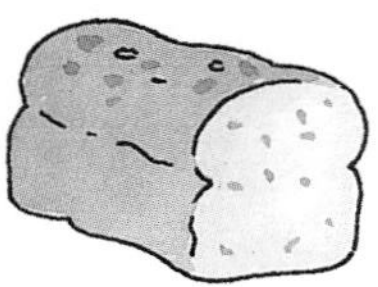

Write the letters *Kk*. • Say the word that names each picture. • Listen for the sound at the beginning of each word. • Draw a circle around each picture whose name begins with the same sound as *kite*.

Name ______________________________

2.

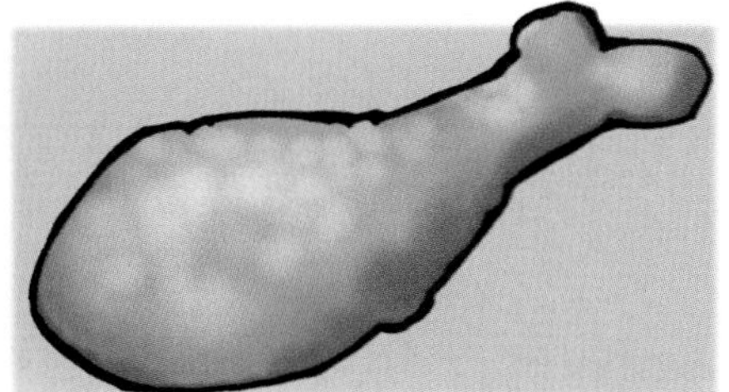

3.

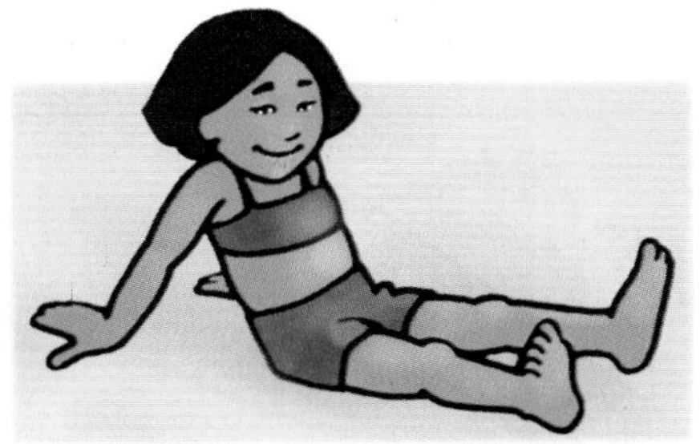

4.

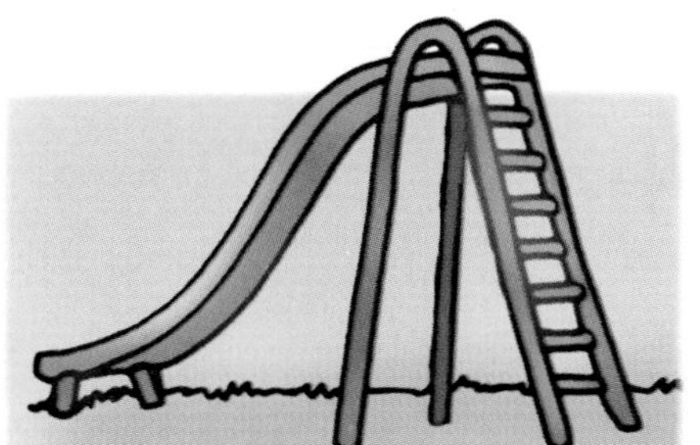

Look at the pictures. In row **1** draw a circle around a place. In row **2** draw a circle around a person. In row **3** draw a circle around a place. In row **4** draw a circle around a thing.

___ck

Name ____________________

1.

2.

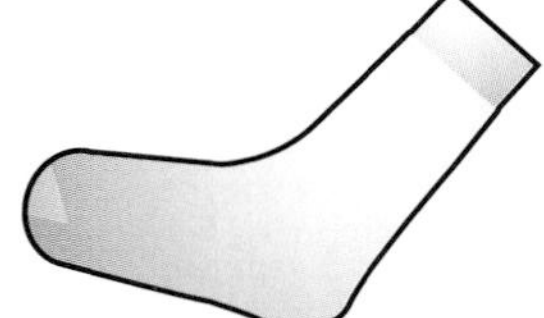

3.

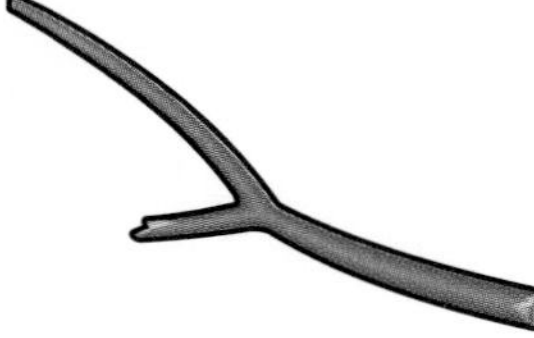

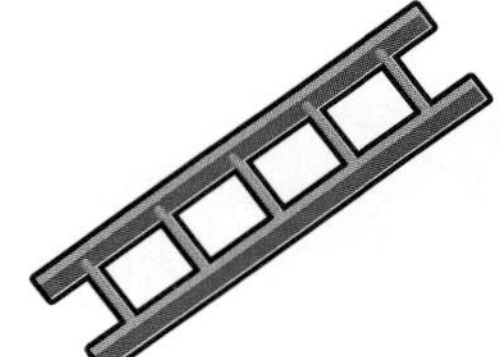

4.

Say the name of each picture. • Draw a circle around each picture whose name has the same ending sound as *sock*. • Write the letters *ck*.

Name____

1.

2.

3.

Look at the pictures. • Draw a circle around the picture that shows the beginning of the story. • Draw a line under the picture that shows the middle of the story. • Draw a square around the picture that shows the end of the story.

Name ____________________

1. k

k		

2. ck

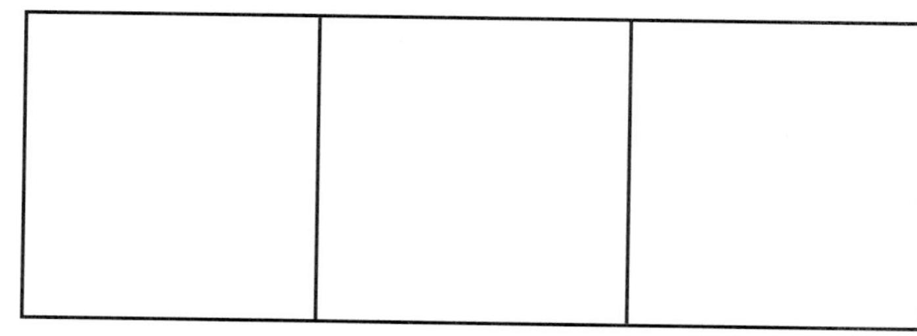

3. ck

4. ck

Trace the letter or letters. Say the word that names the picture. Write the letter or letters in the correct box to show if you hear the sound /k/*k* or /k/*ck* at the beginning, middle, or the end of the word.

Name

for

1. The pup is for me.

2. The cat is for you.

3. The duck is for Kim.

4. The cap is for Dad.

Read the sentence. • Then draw a line under the word *for* in the sentence.

Name ____________________

1. l o ck 

2. p a ck

3. d u ck

4. k i ck

Blend the sounds and say the word. • Write the word. • Draw a circle around the picture that goes with the word.

"I did," said Kim.

Tom Is Sick

"I can pick up the cap."

"I can pick up for Tom."

"Tom is sick," said Kim.

"Did you pick up?" said Tom.

"I can pick up the sock."

"I can pick up the duck."

Name ______________________________

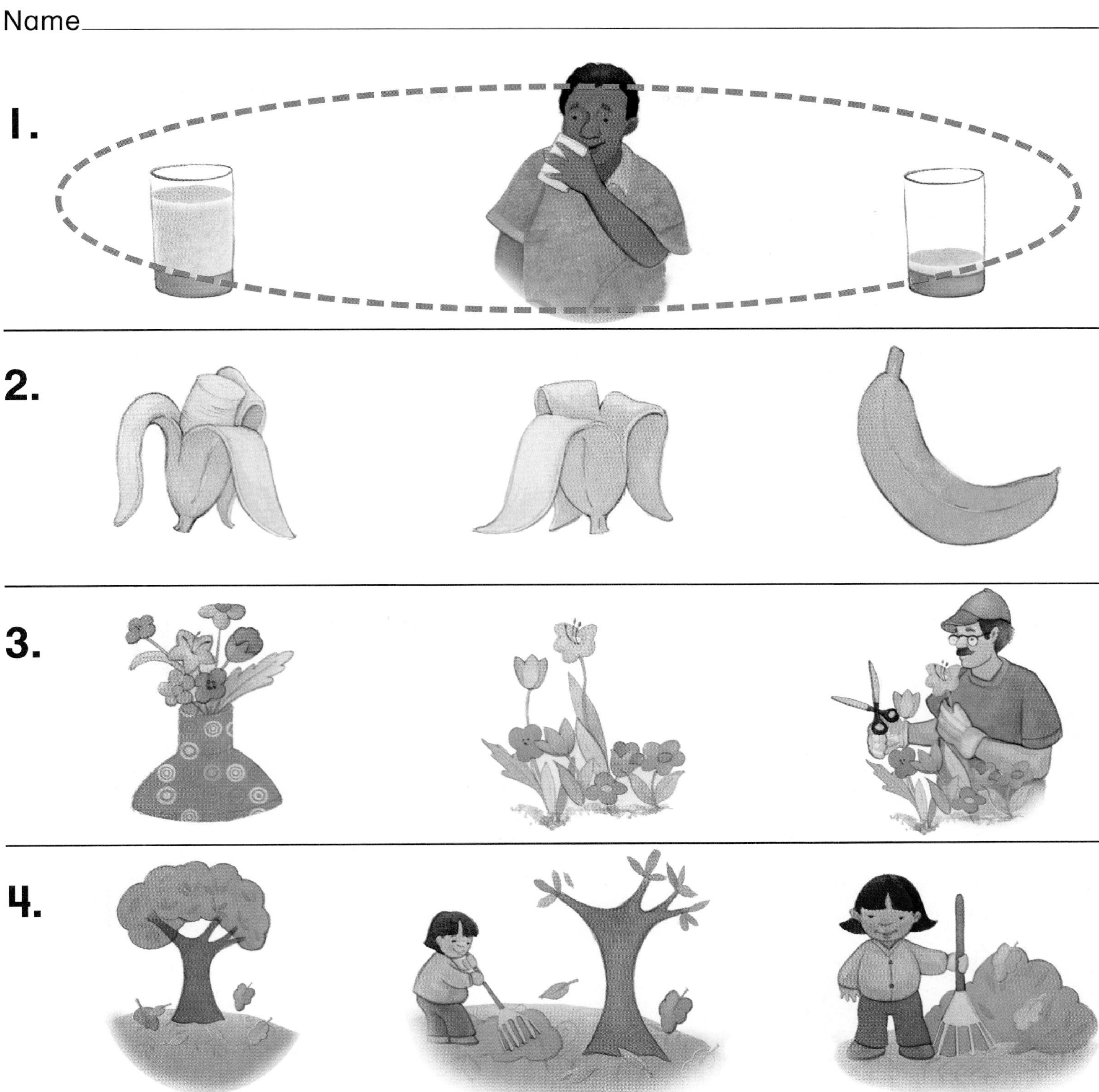

Look at pictures in each row. Draw a circle around each row of pictures that tells a story from beginning to middle to end. Cross out each row of pictures that does not tell a story in correct order.

Name________________________________

1. 

can cat

cat

2. 

run rat

3. 

rip lip

4. 

lock sock

Draw a circle around the word that names the picture. • Say the word. • Then write the word.

Name____

1.

The duck is for you.

2.

The cat is for me.

3.

The pup is for you and me.

Read each sentence. **1.** Draw a line under the word *for*. **2.** Draw a line under the word *me*. **3.** Draw a line under the word *you*.

Gg

Name________________________________

1.    

2.    

3.   

4.   

Write the letters *Gg*. Say the word that names each picture. Circle each picture whose name begins with the same sound as *gift*.

Name

Look at the pictures. In row **1** draw a circle around the person. In row **2** draw a circle around the person. In row **3** draw a circle around a place. In row **4** draw a circle around a thing.

Name ______________________

1.

g

2.

3.

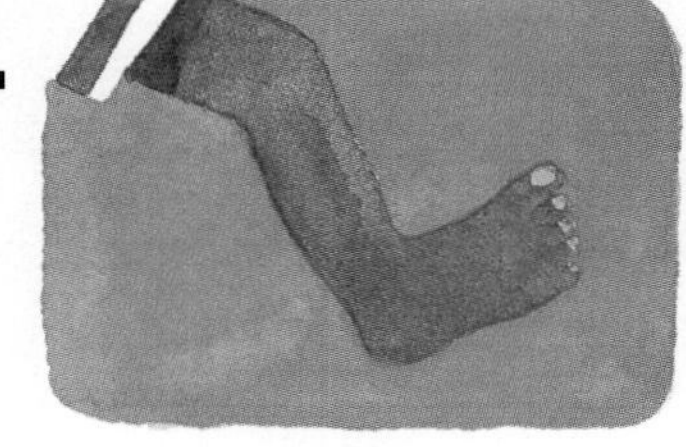
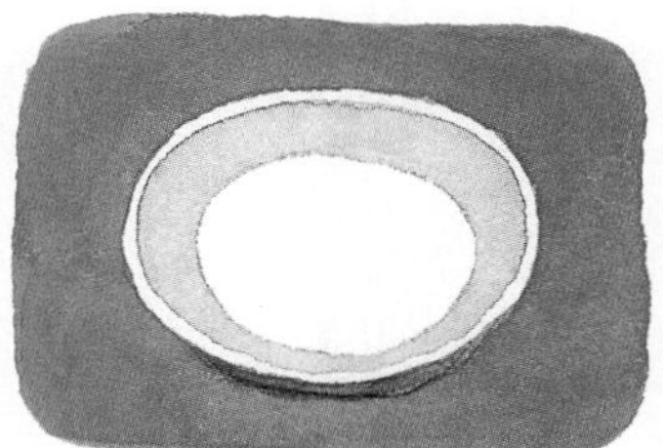

4.

Say the name of each picture. • Draw a circle around each picture whose name has the same ending sound as *frog*. • Write the letter *g*.

Name ______________________________

Circle the pictures of the person and animal that are in the story "Any Kind of Dog." Then, draw a picture to show what the story is about.

Name

1. g

g

2. g

3. g

4. g

Trace the letter. Say the word that names the picture. Write the letter in the correct box to show if you hear the sound /g/*g* at the beginning, middle, or the end of the word.

Name ____________________

he

1\.

Is he mad at Kim?

2\.

He is not mad at Kim.

3\.

Did he sit on the log?

4\.

He sat on the log.

Read the sentence. • Then draw a line under the word *he* in the sentence.

Name ______________________________

1. p i g

pig

2. l o g

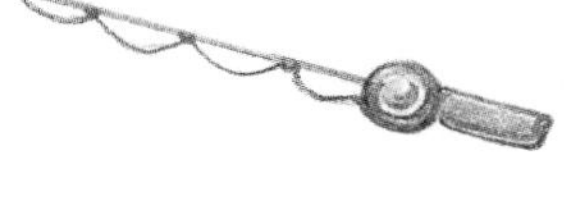

3. r a g

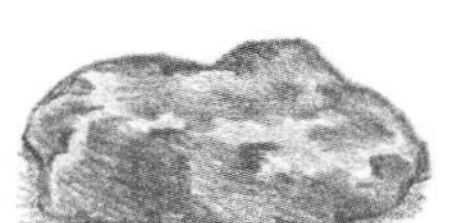

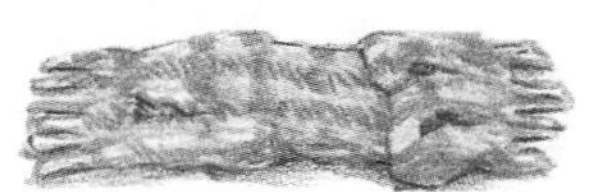

4. m u g

Blend the sounds and say the word. • Write the word. • Draw a circle around the picture that goes with the word.

Mom and Pug sip.

He Is Pug

“For me?” said Mom.

He got a mug.

Pug got a pot.

2

"For you," said Pug.

7

He got Mom up.

4

Mom is in luck.

5

Name____

Circle the pictures of the animals that are in the story "He Is Pug." Then, draw a picture to show what the story is about.

Name ______________________

1. 

man mug

mug

2. 

sun sick

3. 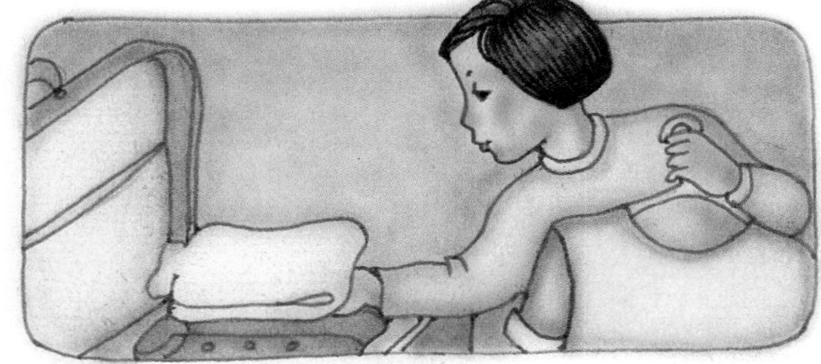

pack pin

4. 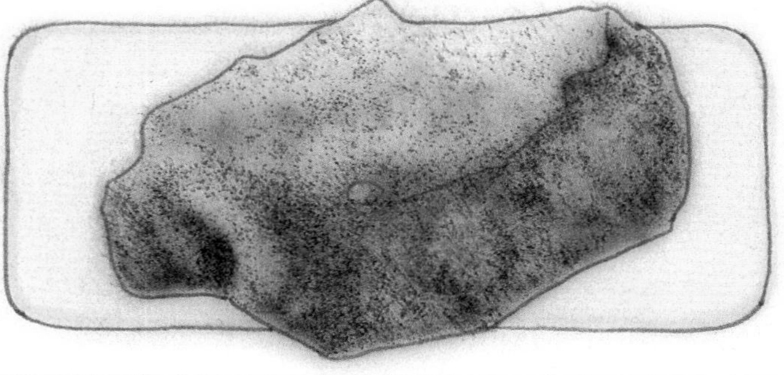

run rock

Draw a circle around the word that names the picture. • Say the word. • Then write the word.

Name ______________________________

1.

He got a mug for Kim.

2.

That mug is for Kim.

3.

Kim said, "It is for me."

Read each sentence. **1.** Draw a line under the word *he.* **2.** Draw a line under the word *is.* **3.** Draw a line under the word *for.*

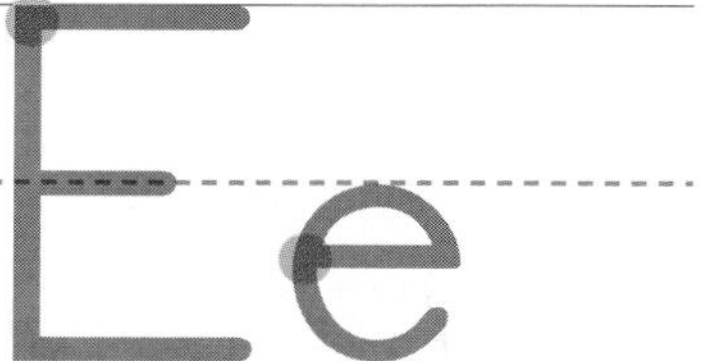

Name

1.

2.

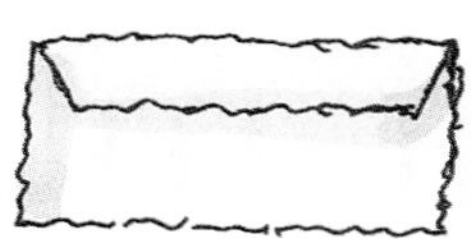

3.

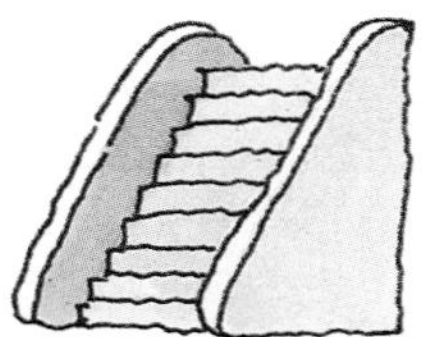

4.

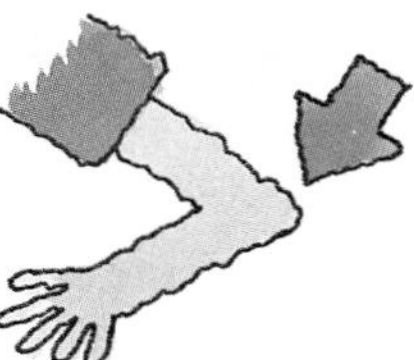

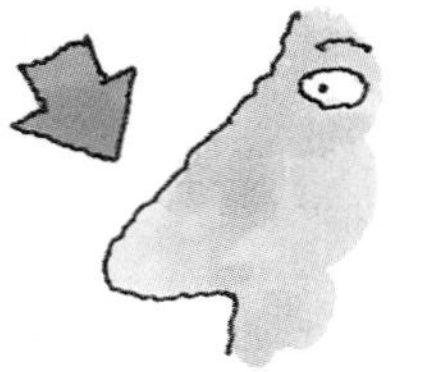

Write the letters *Ee*. • Say the word that names each picture. • Listen for the sound at the beginning of each word. • Draw a circle around each picture whose name begins with the same sound as *egg*.

Name ______________________________

1. ten Sam pick

2. kick the Nan

3. nut run you

4. cat I cut

Circle the word that describes an action.

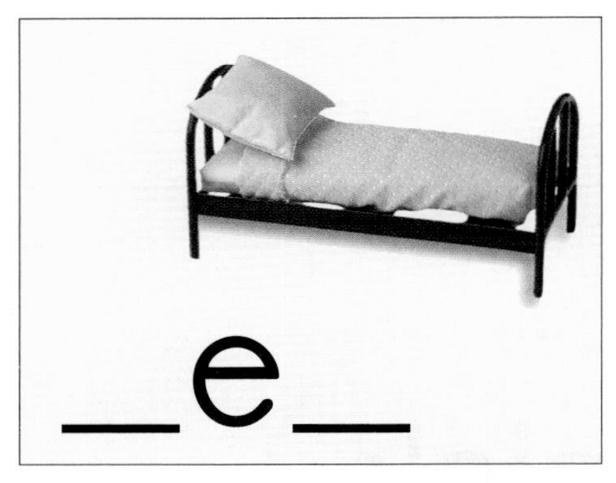

Name

e

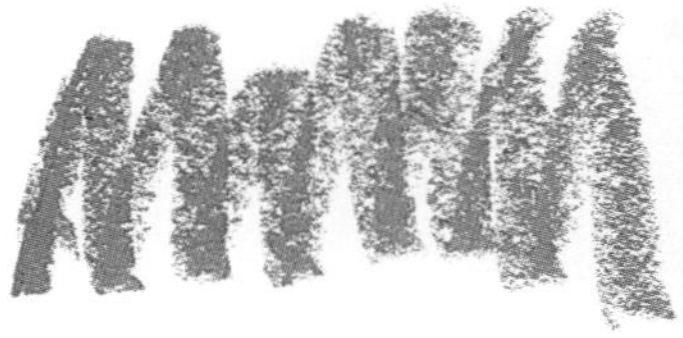

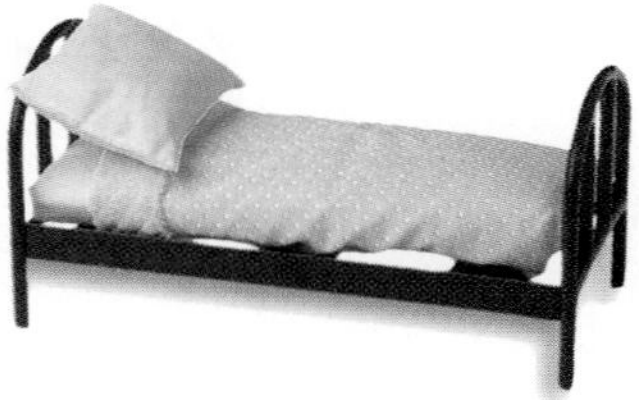

Write the letter *e*. • Say the word that names each picture. • Listen for the sound in the middle of each word. • Circle each picture whose name has the same middle sound as *bed*.

Name ____________________

1.

2.

3.

4.

Look at pictures in each row. Draw a circle around each row of pictures that tells a story from beginning to middle to end. Cross out each row of pictures that does not tell a story in correct order.

Name ______________________________

1. e

	e	

2. e

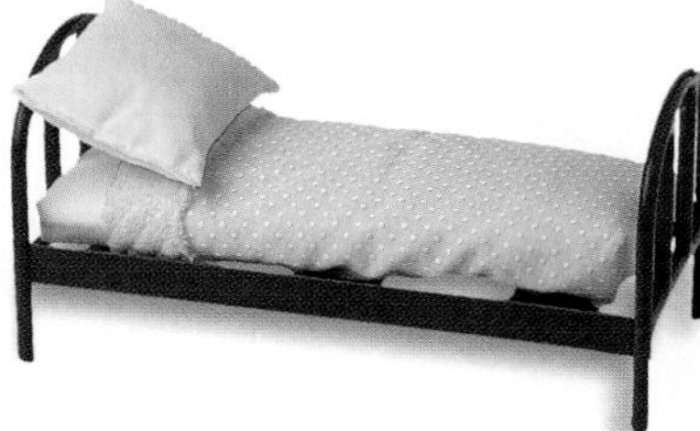

3. e

4. e

Trace the letter. Say the word that names the picture. Write the letter in the correct box to show if you hear the sound /e/*e* at the beginning, middle, or the end of the word.

Name ______________________________

she

1. Did she get a pet?

2. She got a pet.

3. Did she get a cat?

4. She got a tan pup.

Read the sentence. • Then draw a line under the word *she* in the sentence.

Name ______________________________

1. n e t

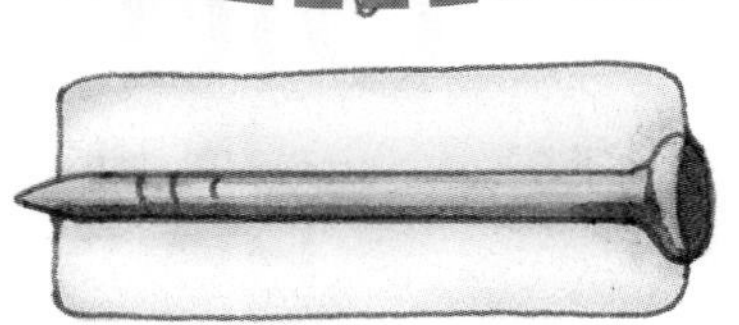

2. m e n

3. p e n

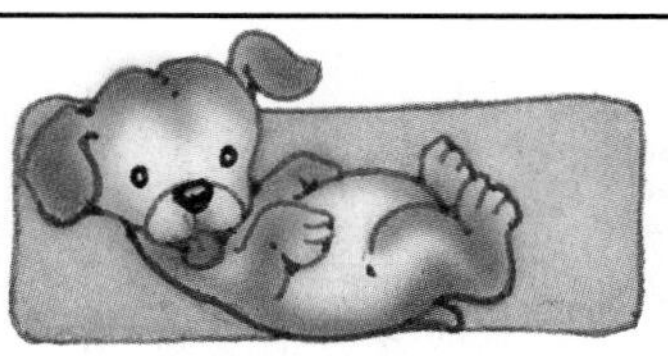

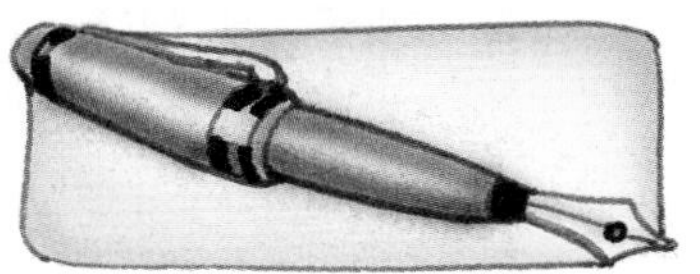

4. l e g

Blend the sounds and say the word. • Write the word. • Draw a circle around the picture that goes with the word.

She and I have fun!

A Pet for Ken

We can go for a dip.

My pup can sit up.

I have a red pup.

We can run and run.

McGraw-Hill School Division

I let my pup lick me.

She can pick up a sock.

Name ____

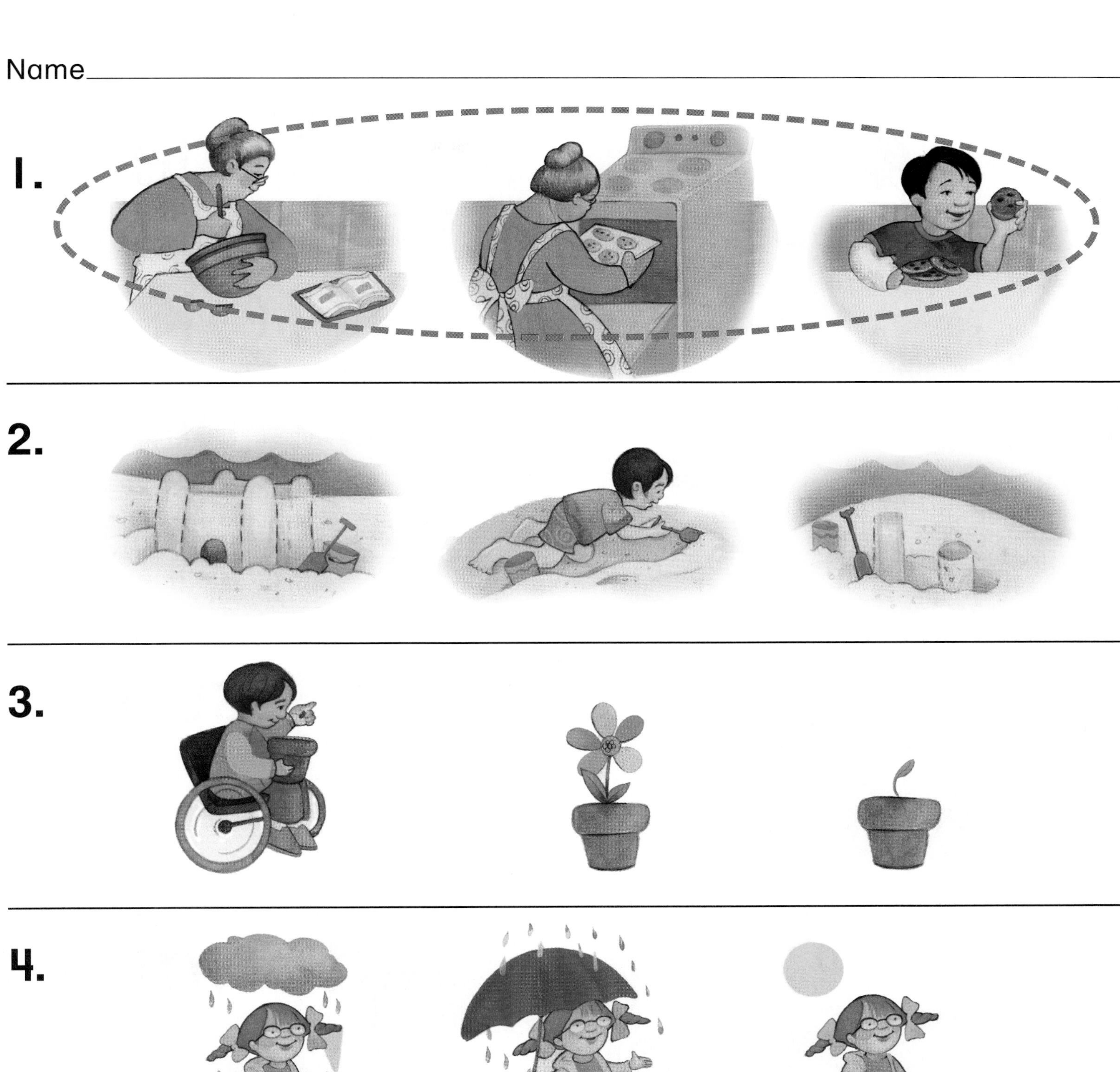

Look at pictures in each row. Draw a circle around each row of pictures that tells a story from beginning to middle to end. Cross out each row of pictures that does not tell a story in correct order.

Name ____________________

1. 

duck den

duck

2. 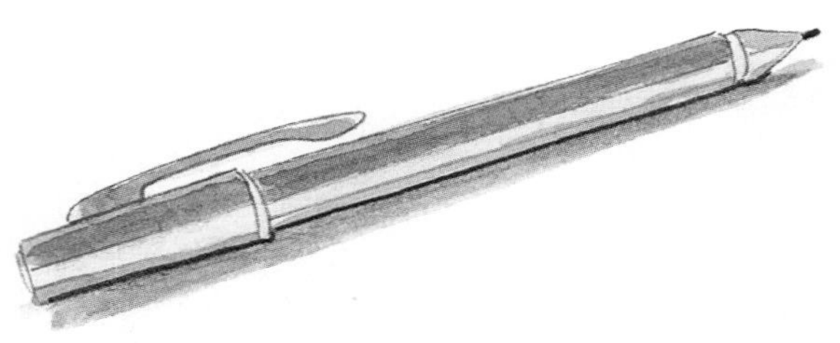

pan pen

3. 

set sun

4. 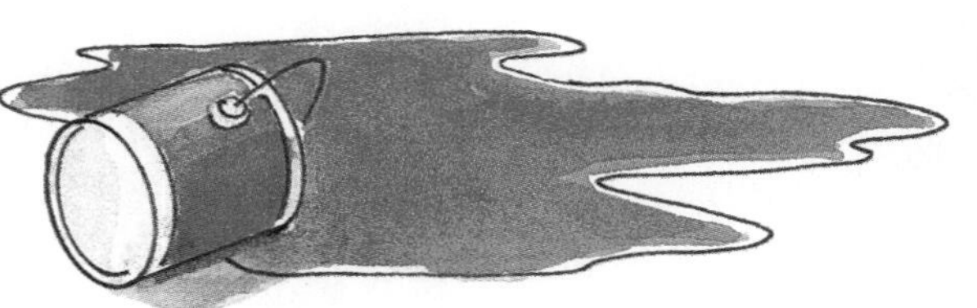

red rat

Draw a circle around the word that names the picture. • Say the word. • Then write the word.

Name ____________________

I.

Did she get a cap for Ron?

2.

She and he got a cap.

3.

That red cap is for Ron.

Read each sentence. **I.** Draw a line under the word *she*. Draw a circle around the word *for*. **2.** Draw a line under the word *he*. **3.** Draw a line under the word *is*.

Bb

Name______________________________

1. Bb

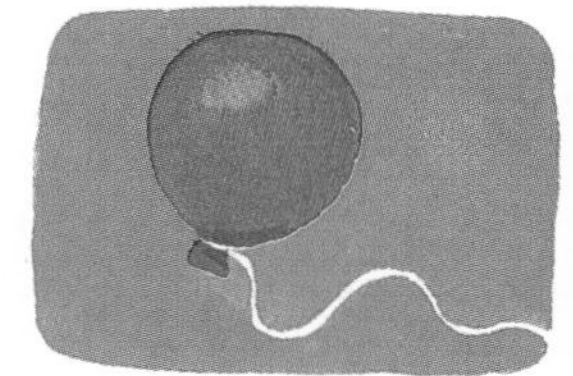
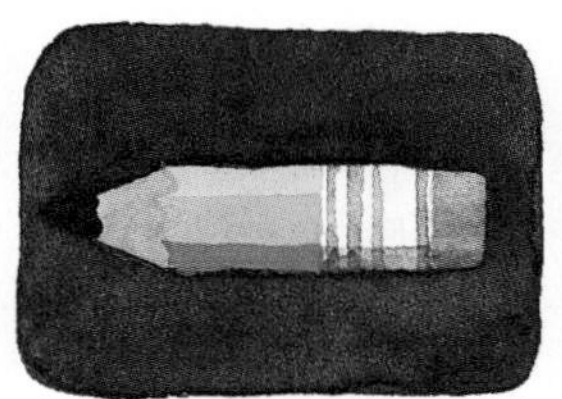

2. 

3.

4.

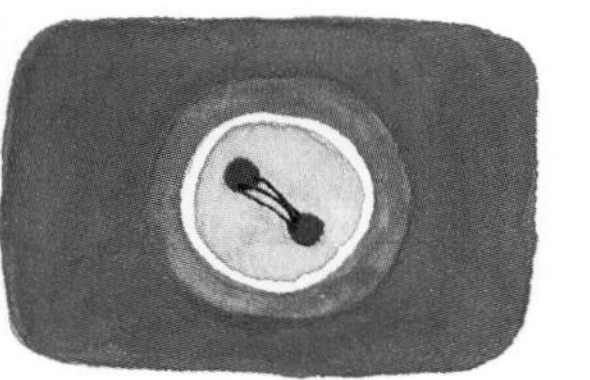

Write the letters *Bb.* • Say the word that names each picture. • Listen for the sound at the beginning of each word. • Circle each picture whose name begins with the same sound as *balloon.*

Name ________________________________

1. Ben dig bad

2. pack my and

3. we go sad

4. Mom red lick

Circle the word that describes an action.

b

Name ____________________

1.  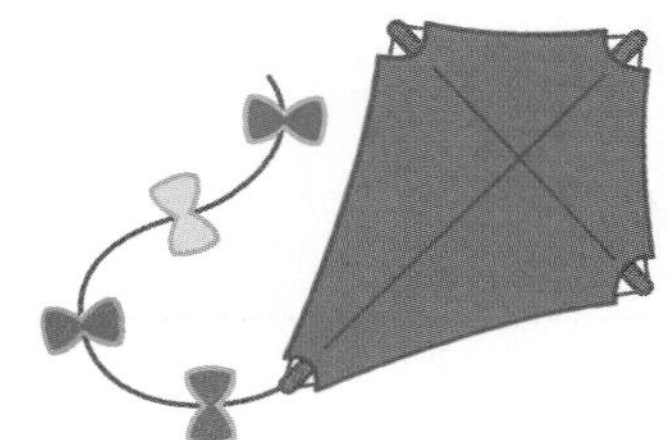  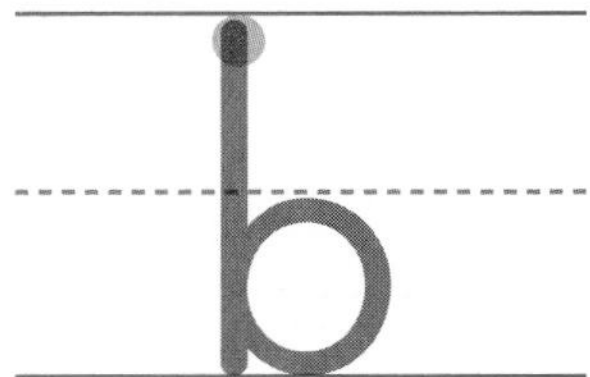

2.   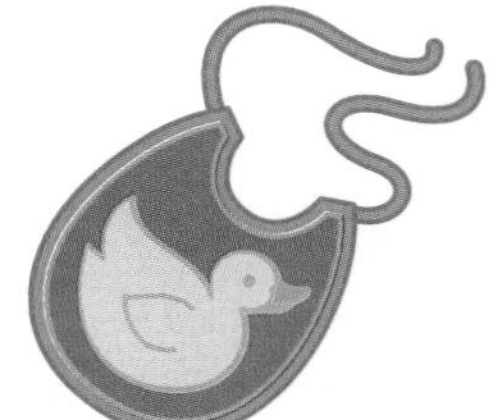

3. 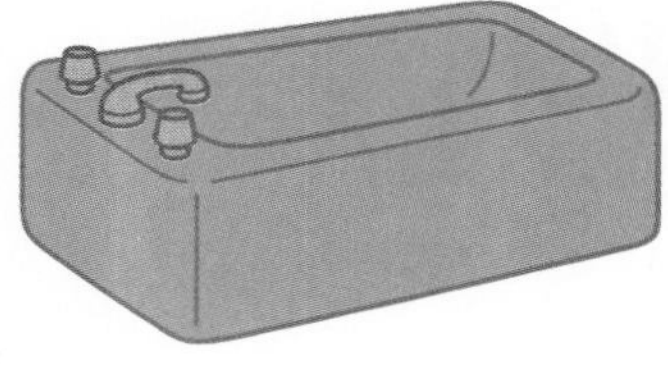  

4.  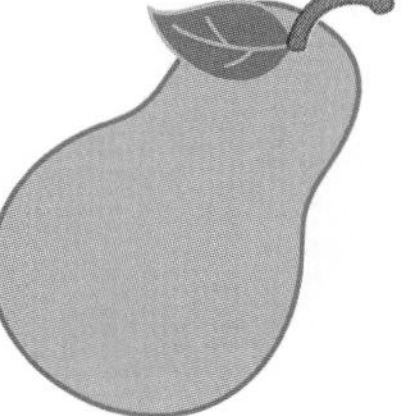 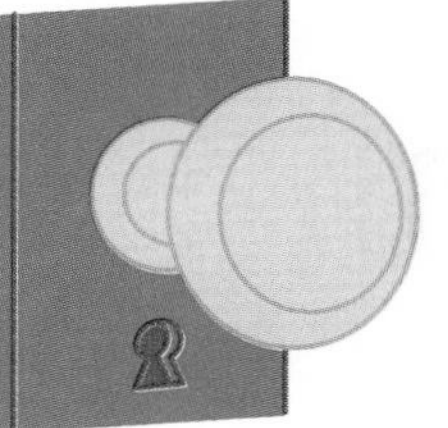

Say the word that names each picture. Circle the pictures whose names have the same ending sound as *tub*. Write the letter *b*.

Name____

Circle the pictures of the animals that are in the story "The Enormous Carrot." Then, draw a picture to show what the story is about.

Name ____________________

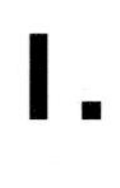

2. 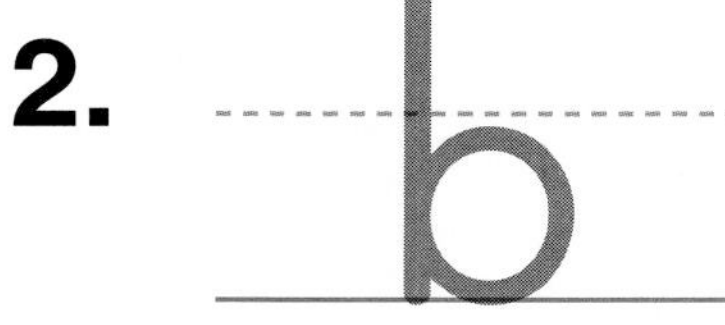

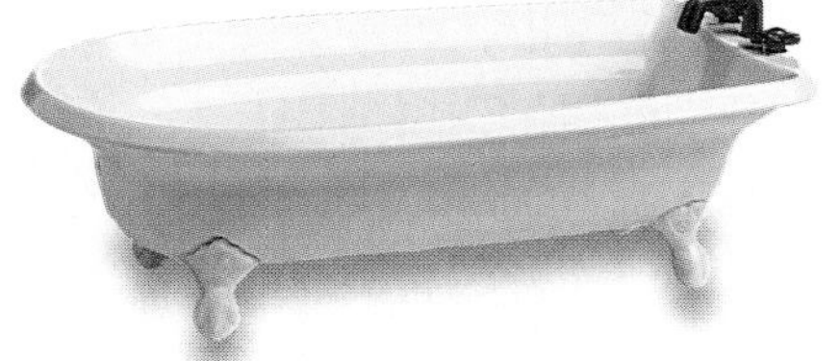

3. 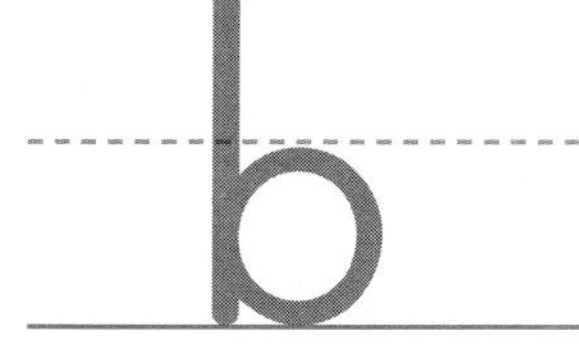

4. 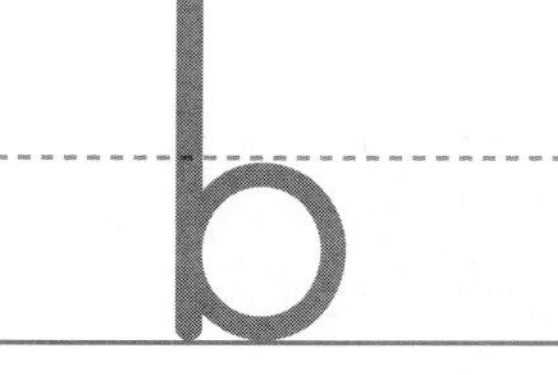

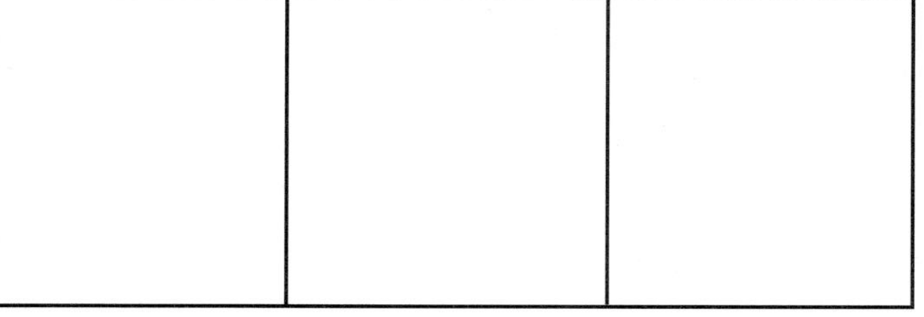

Trace the letter. Say the word that names each picture. Write the letter in the correct box to show if you hear the sound /b/b at the beginning, middle, or the end of the word.

Name ____________________

has

1. Ben has a big cat.

2. The cat has a red tag.

3. Pam has a big pup.

4. The pup has a tan tag.

Read the sentence. • Then draw a line under the word *has* in the sentence.

Name

1. b a g

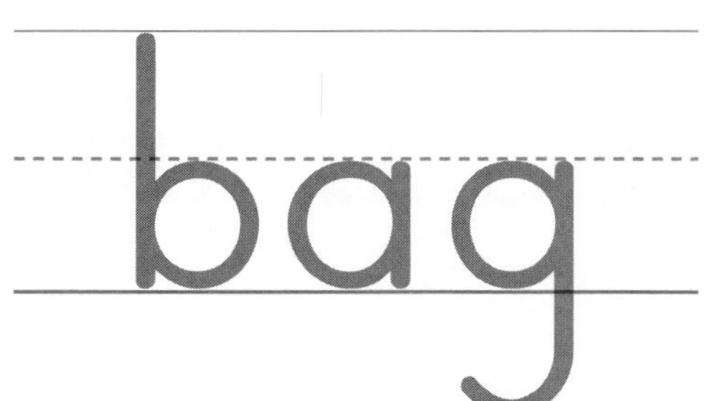

2. b e d

3. b i b

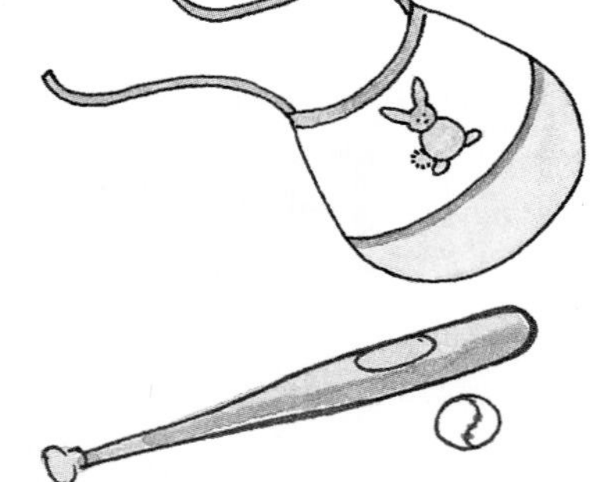

4. c u b

Blend the sounds and say the word. • Write the word. • Draw a circle around the picture that goes with the word.

The big bug has fun.

A Big Bug

Meg has a bug net.

It is a big bug!

A bug is on the rug.

Meg can let the bug go.

Mom can not get the bug.

But Meg can get the bug.

Name

Circle the pictures of the people and animal that are in the story "A Big Bug." Then, draw a picture to show what the story is about.

Name____________________

1. 

bat bet

bat

2. 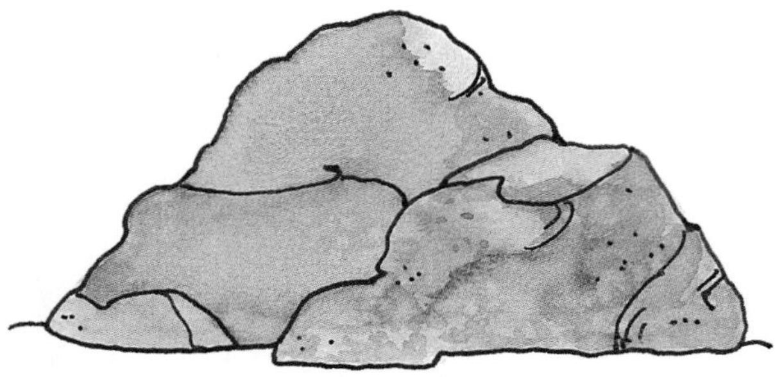

rock rod

3. 

tug ten

4. 

pin pig

Draw a circle around the word that names the picture. • Say the word. • Then write the word.

Name ____________________

1\.

Ken has a mug for me.

2\.

He has a big bag for Nan.

3\.

She has a red fan for me.

Read each sentence. **1.** Draw a line under the word *has*. **2.** Draw a line under the words *he* and *for*. **3.** Draw a line under the words *she* and *me.*

Name________________________

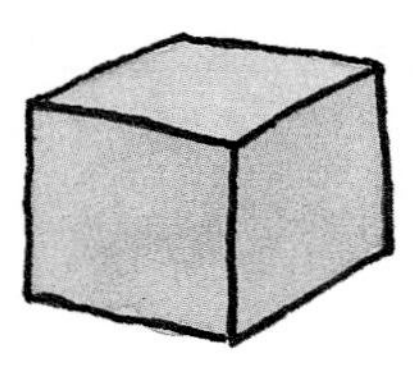

g

Say the name of each picture. • Then write the letter for the sound you hear at the beginning of the picture name.

Name ____________________

1. Tom 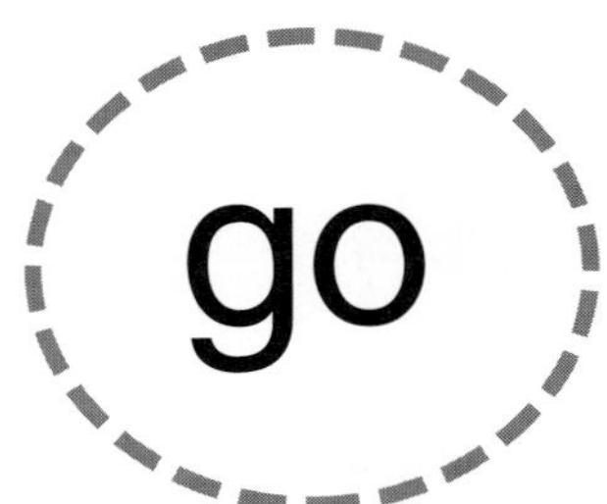 cap

2. kick bat Pam

3. dig Mom Nan

4. Dad den sit

Draw a circle around the word that describes an action. • Draw a line under the words that name a person, place or thing.

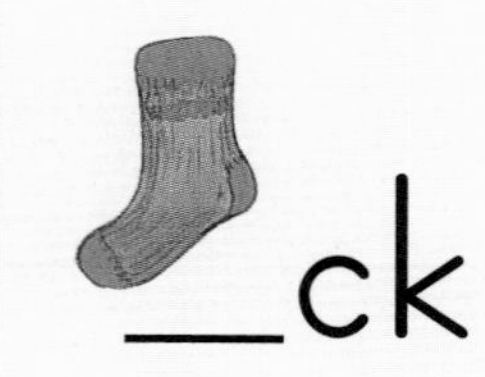

__ck

__g

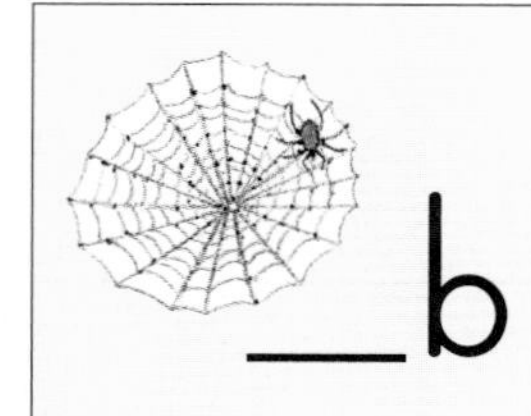

__b

Name ____________________

g

Say the name of each picture. • Then write the letter or letters for the sound you hear at the end of the picture name.

Name ____________________

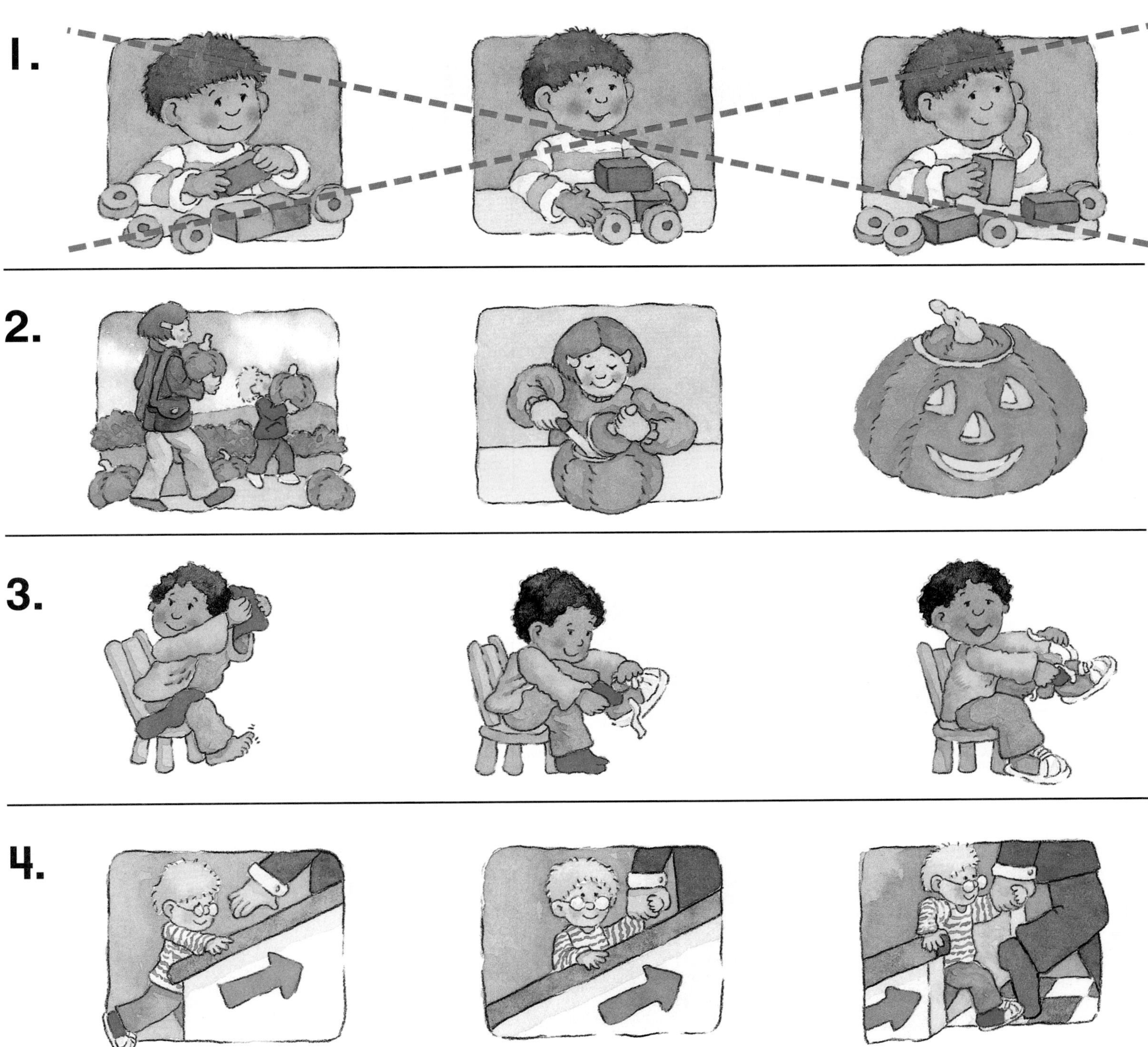

Look at pictures in each row. Draw a circle around each row of pictures that tells a story from beginning to middle to end. Cross out each row of pictures that does not tell a story in correct order.

Name ____________________

1. k

k		

2. b

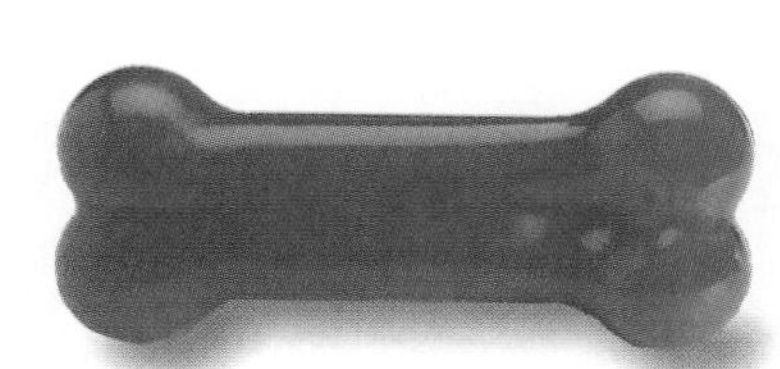

3. ck

4. g

Trace the letter. Say the word that names each picture. Write the letter in the correct box to show if you hear the sound /k/*k*, /k/*ck*, /g/*g*, or /b/*b* at the beginning, middle, or the end of the word.

Name ______________________________

1. has she for he

2. she he for has

3. he has she for

4. for she he has

Read the four words in each row. **1.** Draw a circle around the word *has*. **2.** Draw a circle around the word *he*. **3.** Draw a circle around the word *for*. **4.** Draw a circle around the word *she*.

Name ________________________________

1. K i m

Kim

2. s o ck

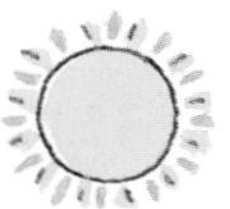

3. t u b

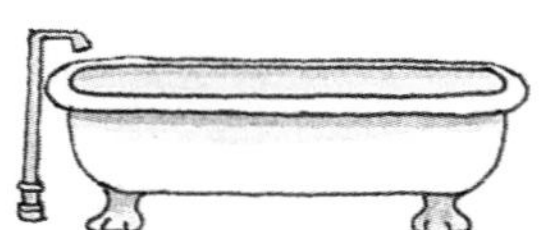

4. r u g

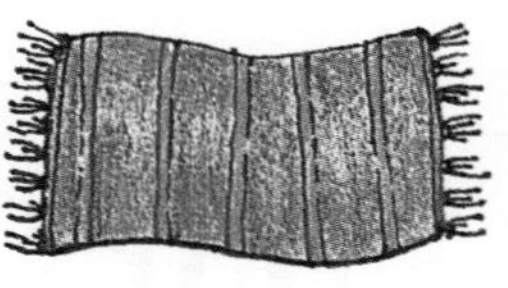

Blend the sounds and say the word. • Write the word. • Draw a circle around the picture that goes with the word.

Pup and Cat have fun!

Pup and Cat

She is not a big cat.

He is a big pup!

Kim has a pup.

2

Kim and Ben have fun.

7

Pup can sit up for Kim.

4

Ben has a tan cat.

5

Name ____________________

Circle the pictures of the animals that are in the story "Pup and Cat."
Then, draw a picture to show what the story is about.

Name____

1. 

nut net

net

2. 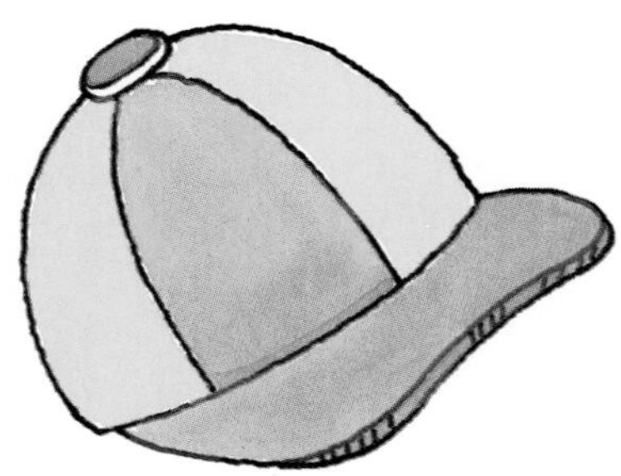

cot cap

3. 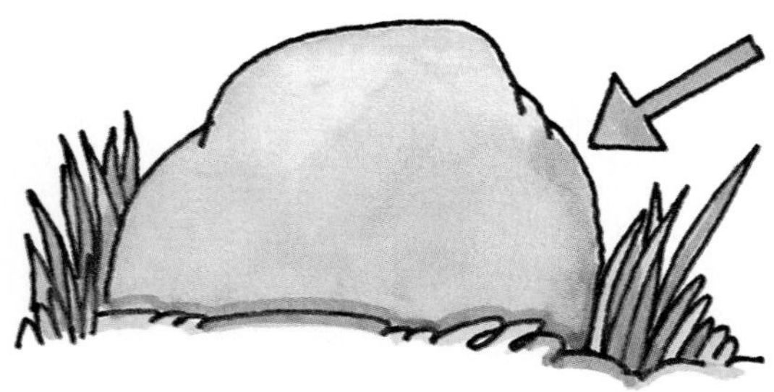

rock rip

4. 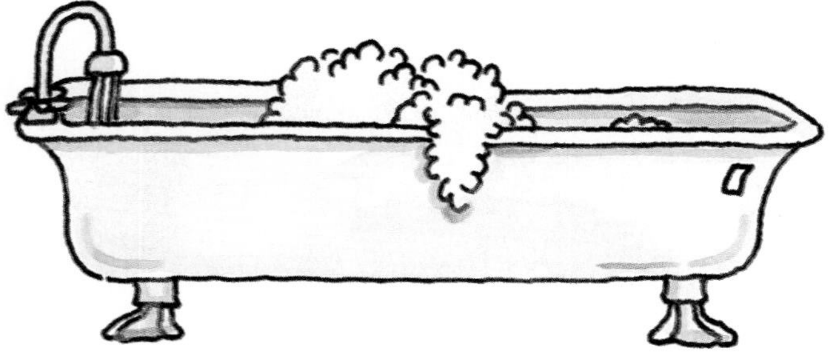

ten tub

Draw a circle around the word that names the picture. • Say the word. • Then write the word.

Name ____________________

1. she	he said she has
2. for	my for have you
3. he	he she the me
4. has	are said that has

Say the first word in the row. • Draw a circle around the word where you see it in the same row.

Hh

Name ______________________________

1. Hh

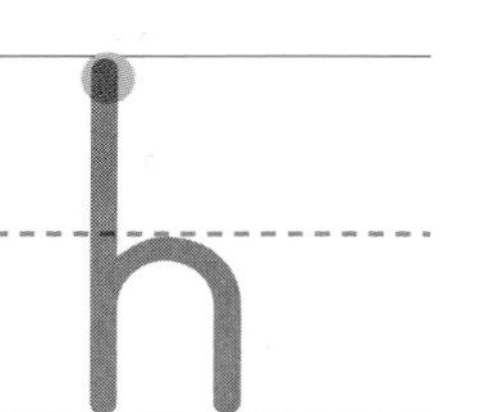

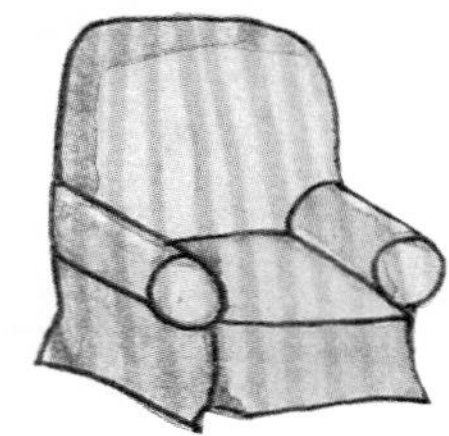

2. Hh

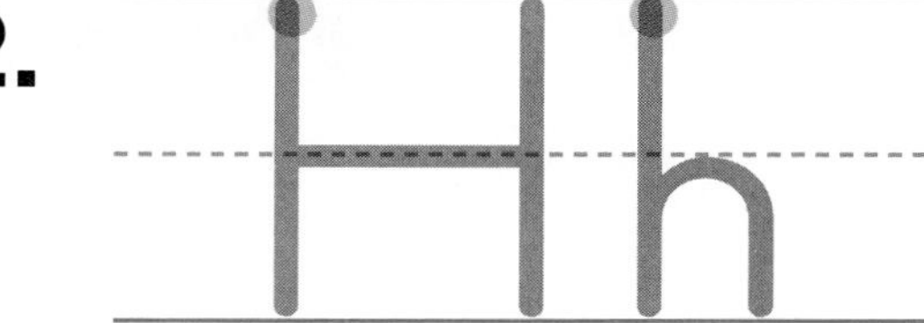
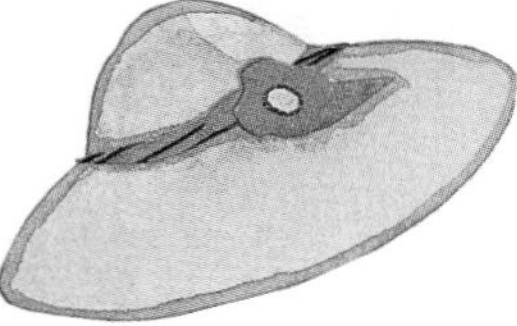

3.

4.

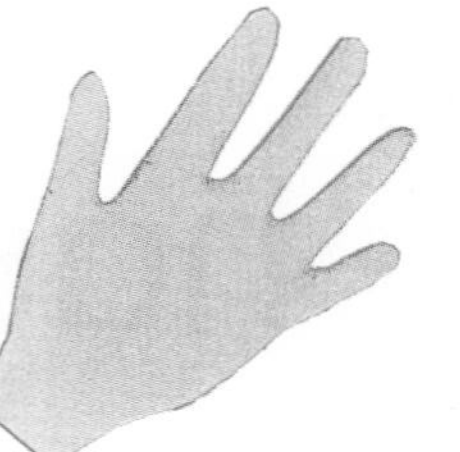

Write the letters *Hh*. • Say the word that names each picture. • Listen for the sound at the beginning of each word. • Draw a circle around each picture whose name begins with the same sound as *hand*.

Name

1.

2.

3.

4.

Color the shapes that are the same in each row.

Name

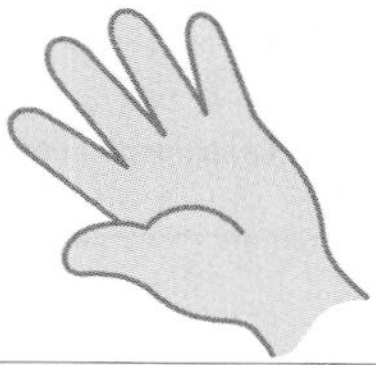

Hh

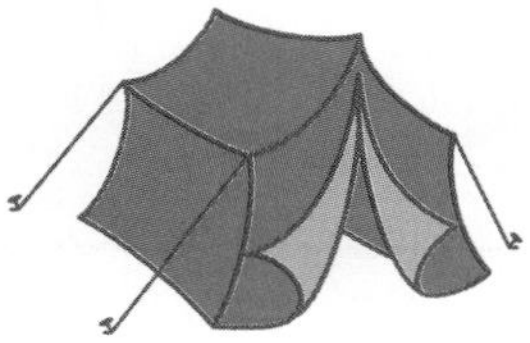

Say the word that names the picture. If the word begins with the same sound as *hen,* write the letters *Hh* on the line.

Name ____________________

Look at the first picture on the left. The boy's actions will cause something to happen. Circle one picture in the row that shows what will happen next. Do the same for the rest of the page.

Name ______________________________

1. h

h		

2.

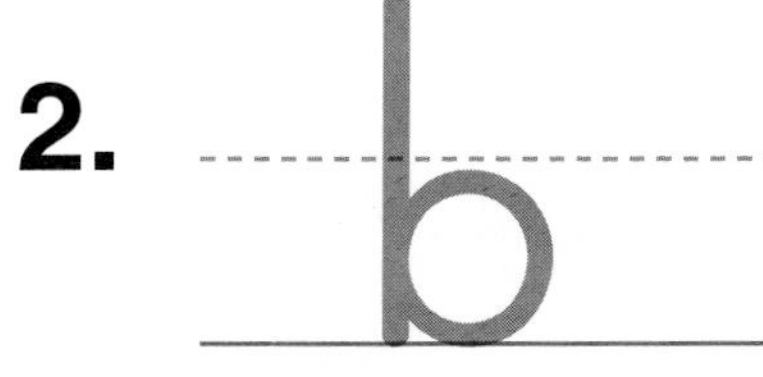

3.

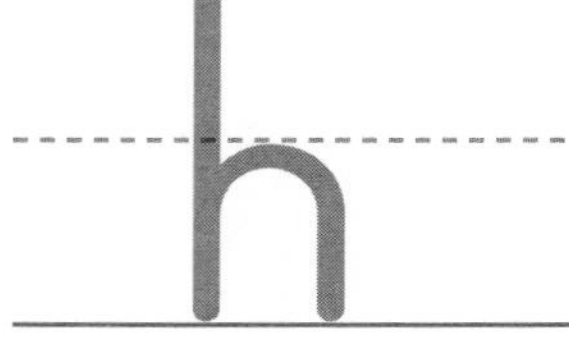

4.

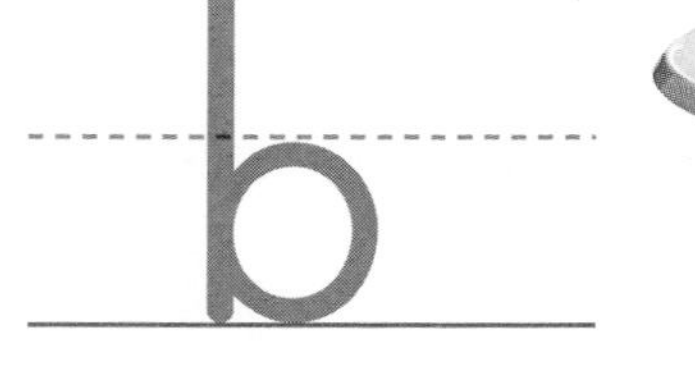

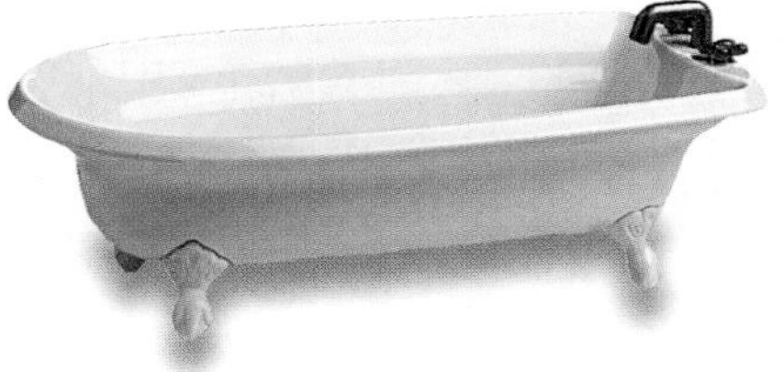

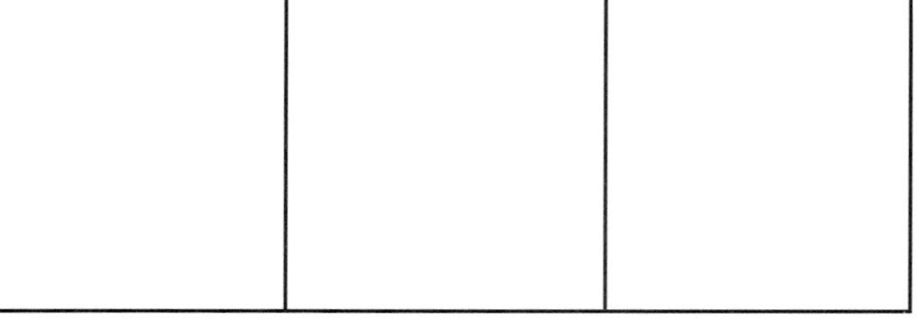

Trace the letter. Say the word that names the picture. Write the letter in the correct box to show if you hear the sound /h/*h* or /b/*b* at the beginning, middle, or the end of the word.

Name ______________________

1. Ken can sit with Kim.

2. Nan can run with Tim.

3. Ken can hop with Pam.

4. I can nap with the cat!

Read the sentence. • Then draw a line under the word *with* in the sentence.

Name ____________________

1. h a t

hat

2. h o p

3. h u g

4. h i t

Blend the sounds and say the word. • Write the word. • Draw a circle around the picture that goes with the word.

Don and the hog
hug and hug!

Hop with a Hog

The big hog can hop
with Don.

He can tag the big hog.

Don has a big hog.

Don and the hog are a big hit.

The big hog has a hat with a dot.

The big hog can hum with Don.

Name ______________________________

Look at the first picture on the left. The actions shown will cause something to happen. Circle one picture in the row that shows what will happen next. Do the same for the rest of the page.

Name ______________________________

1. 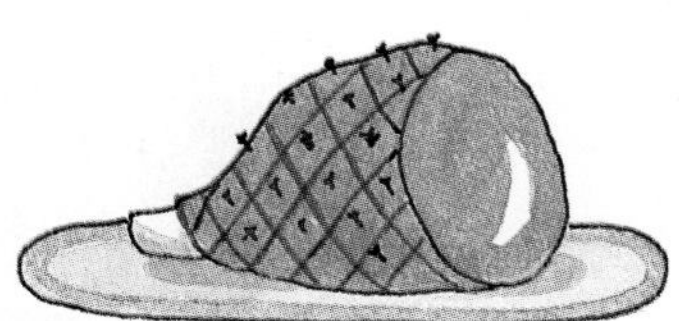

hat ham

ham

2. 

men mop

3. 

duck luck

4. 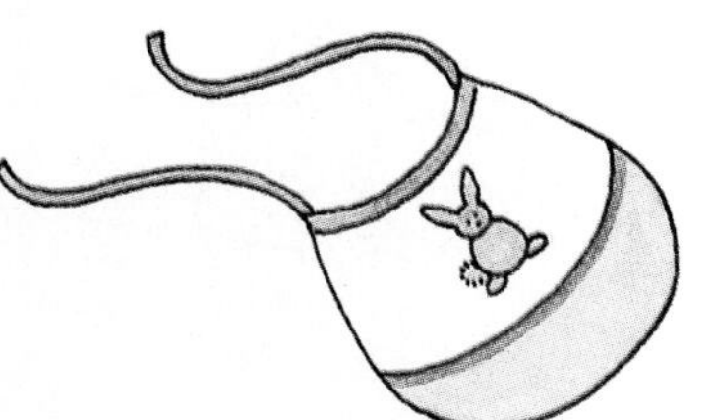

but bib

Draw a circle around the word that names the picture. • Say the word. • Then write the word.

Name________________________________

1. Pam said, "Go to the den."

2. Ben said, "Go with me."

3. Pam and Ben go to the den.

4. I go with Pam and Ben.

Read each sentence. • Draw a circle around the word *go* where you see it in each sentence. **1.** Draw a line under the word *the*. **2.** Draw a line under the words *with* and *me*. **3.** Draw a line under the words *the* and *and*. **4.** Draw a line under the words *with* and *and*.

Ww

Name ______________________________

1. 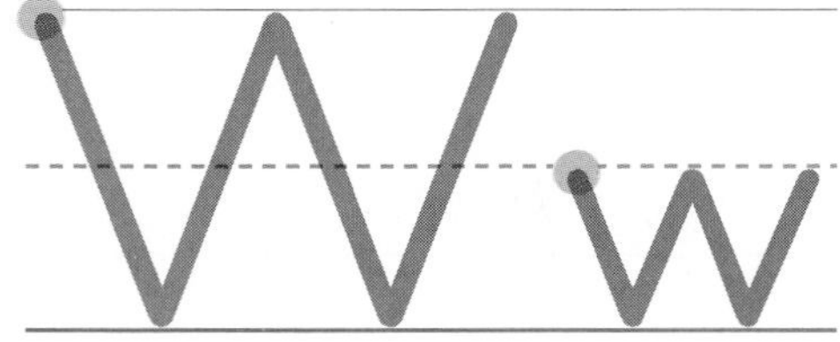

2. 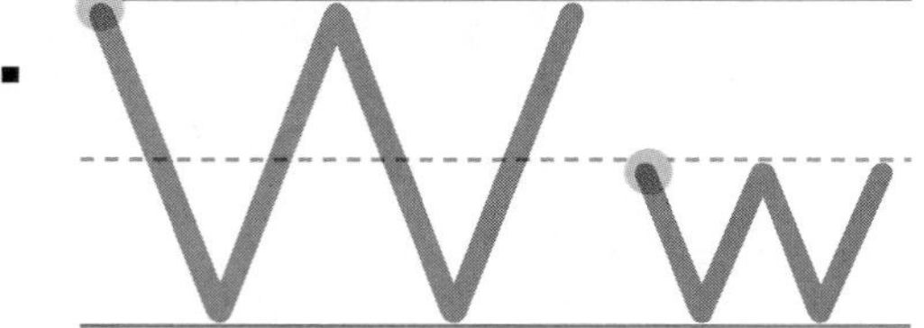
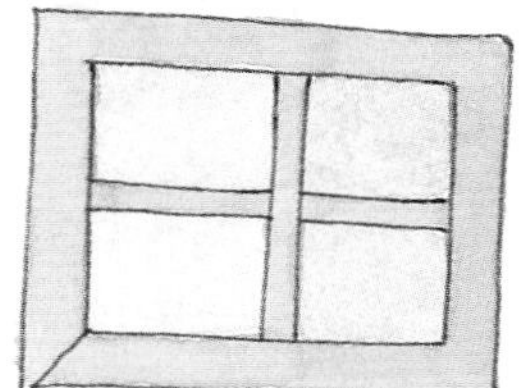

3. 

4. 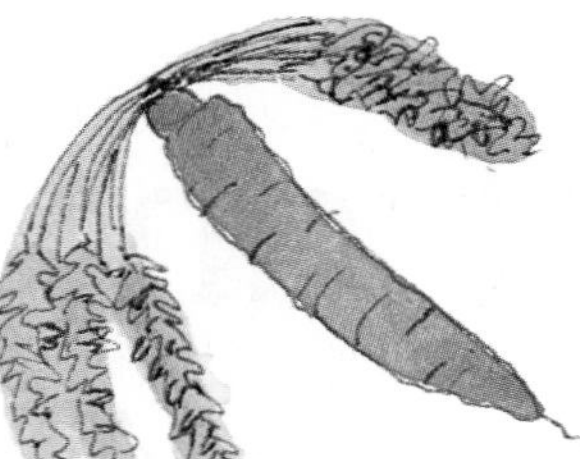
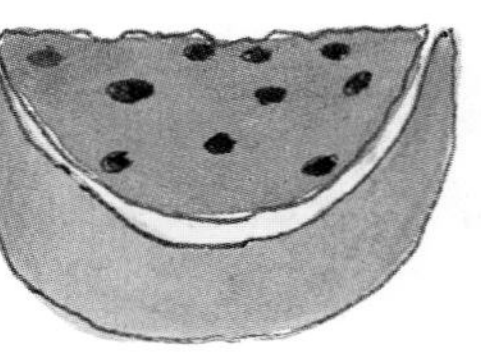
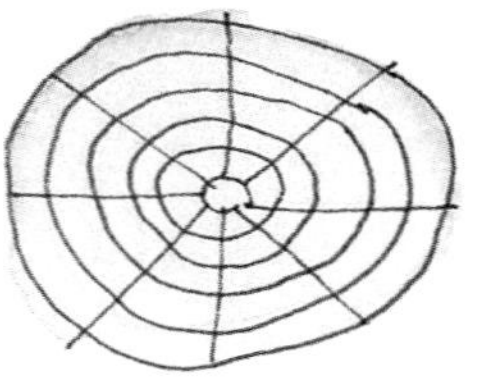

Write the letters *Ww.* • Say the word that names each picture. • Listen for the sound at the beginning of each word. • Draw a circle around each picture whose name begins with the same sound as *window.*

Name ______________________________

Find the squares in the picture. • Color them one color. • Find the rectangles in the picture. • Color them another color.

Name ____________________

Ww

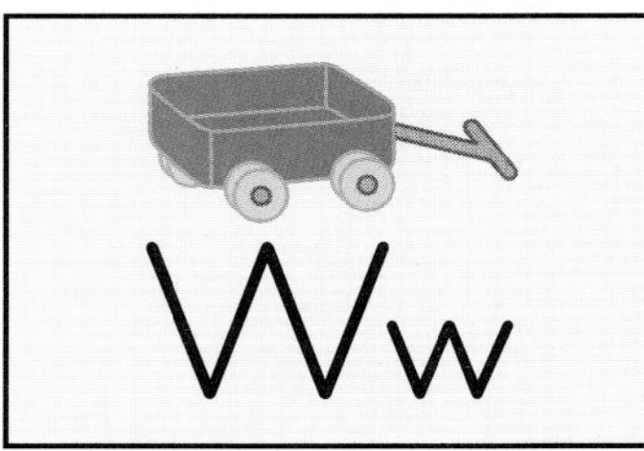

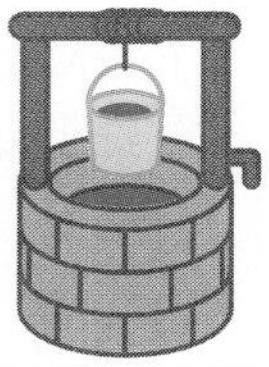

Ww

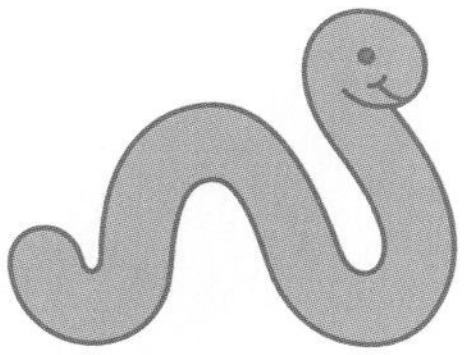

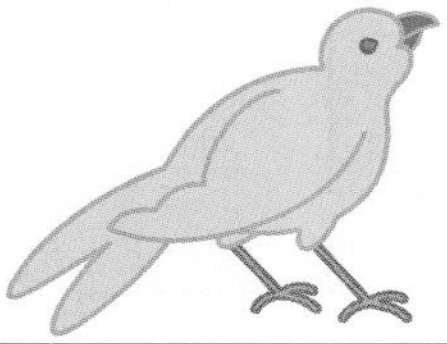

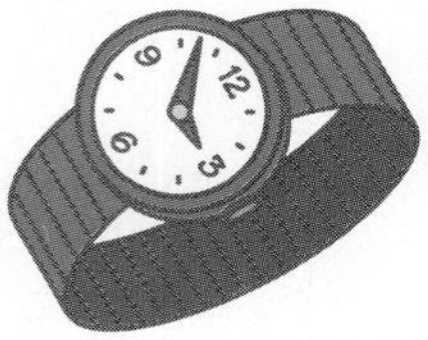

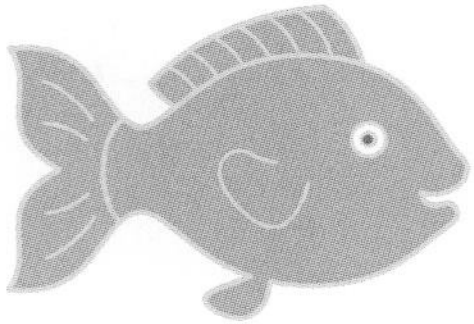

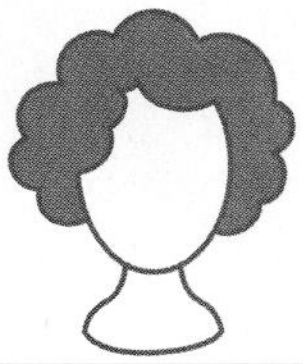

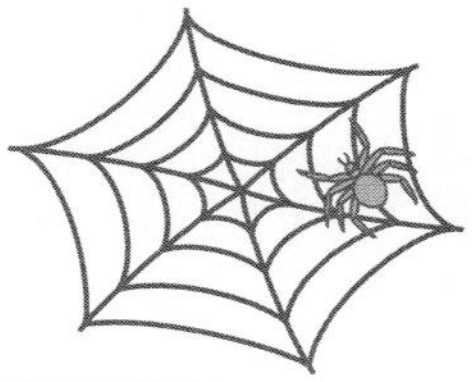

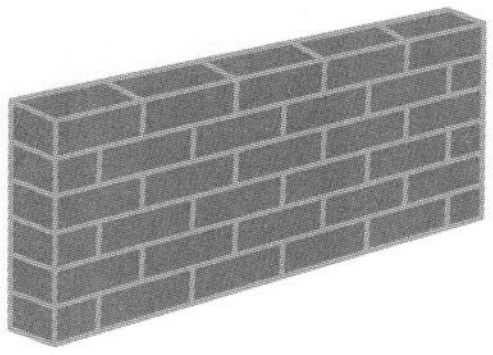

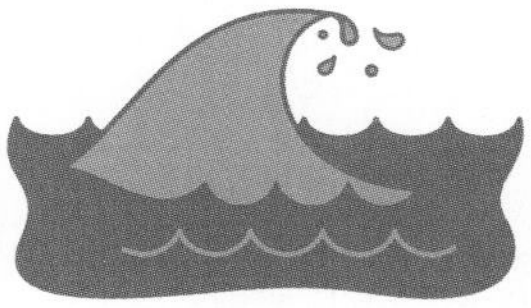

Say the word that names the picture. If the word begins with the same sound as *wagon* write the letters *Ww* on the line.

Name____

1.

2.

3.

Look at the picture on the left. • Draw a circle around the face that shows how the person in the picture is feeling.

Name ______________________________

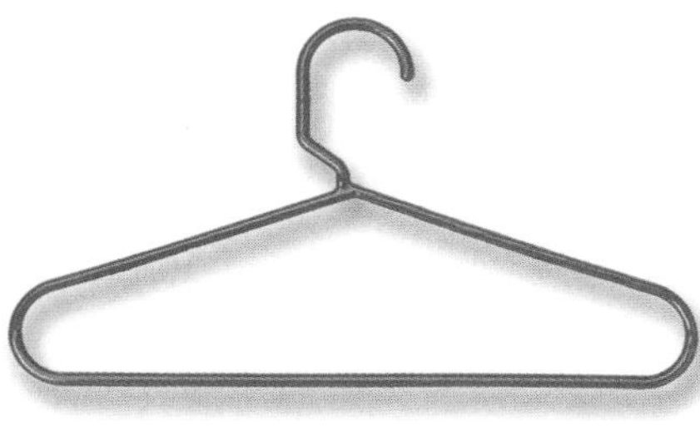

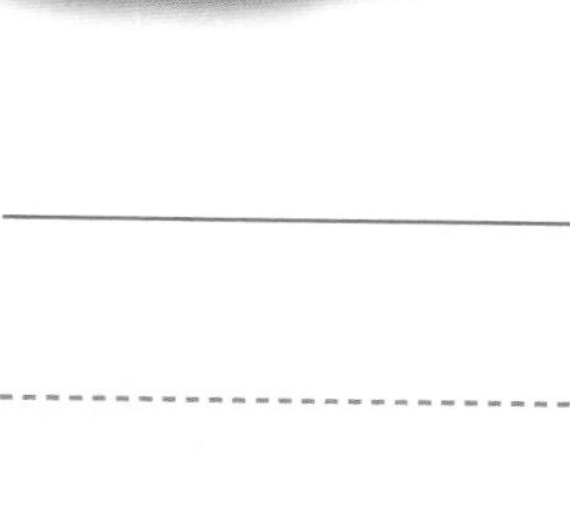

Say the word that names each picture. Then write the letter for the sound you hear at the beginning of the picture name.

Name______________________________

was

1. The hog was in the mud.

2. The duck was wet.

3. The pig was in the pen.

4. The cat was in the den.

Read the sentence. • Then draw a line under the word *was* in the sentence.

Name ______________________________

1.
w e b

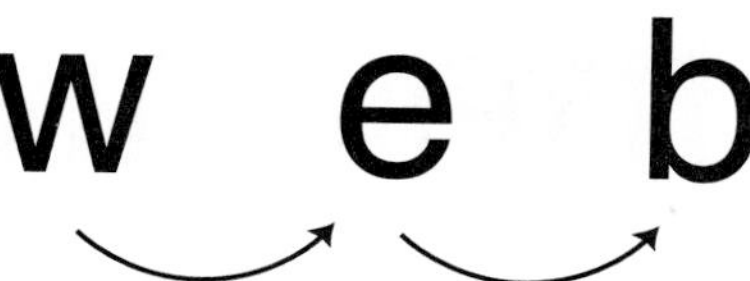

web

2.
w a g

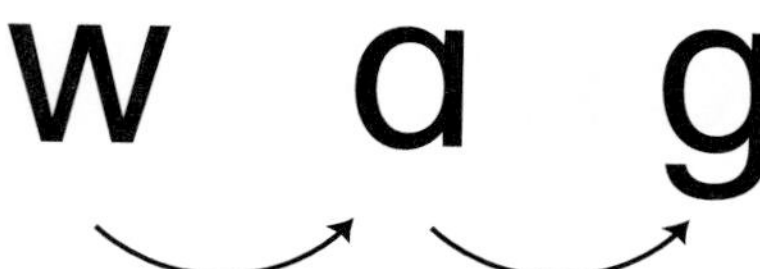

3.
w i g

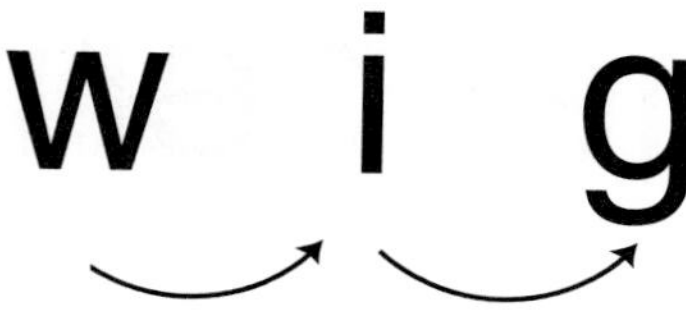

4.
w i n

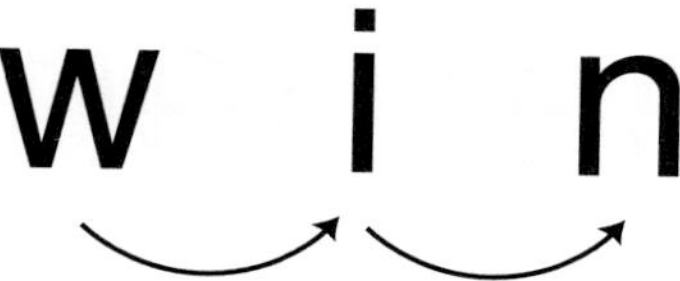

Blend the sounds and say the word. • Write the word. • Draw a circle around the picture that goes with the word.

"We win! We win!"
said Ken.

We Win!

But Ned did not tag
Ken.

Ken was up at bat.

Ken had on a red cap.

Ken ran on and on.

Ken had a hit and ran!

"I can tag him," said Ned.

Name ____________________

1.

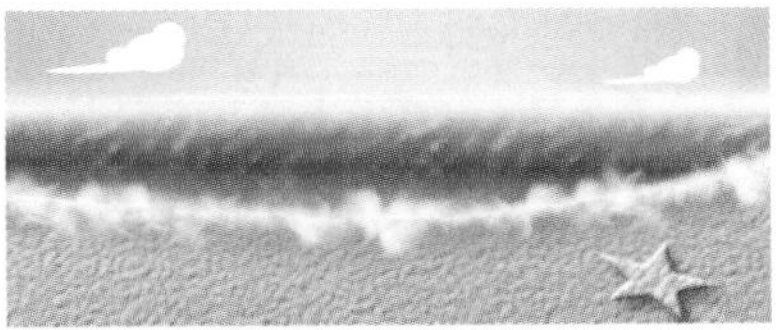

2.

3.

Look at the picture on the left. • Then look at the two pictures on the right. • Draw a line to the picture that shows where the people are going.

Name

1\. 

web win

web

2\. 

ham hot

3\. 

wig wag

4\. 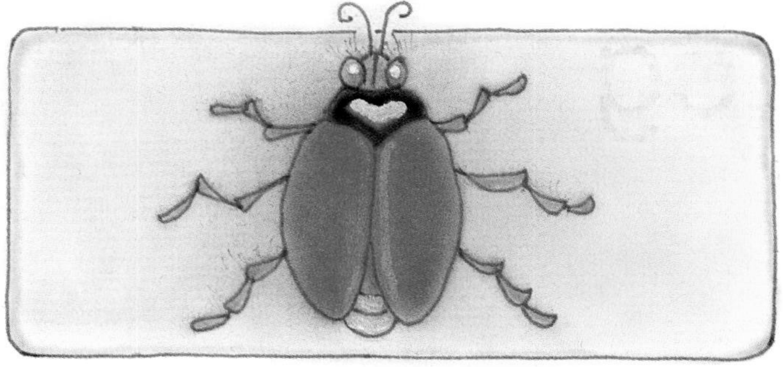

bug beg

Draw a circle around the word that names the picture. • Say the word. • Then write the word.

Name ______________________________

1.

He was a dog.

2.

She was a cat.

3.

I was with a dog and a cat.

Read the sentences. Then do the following: 1. Draw a circle around the words *was* and *he*. 2. Draw a circle around the words *was* and s*he*. 3. Draw a circle around the words *I* and *with*.

Vv

Name________________________________

1. 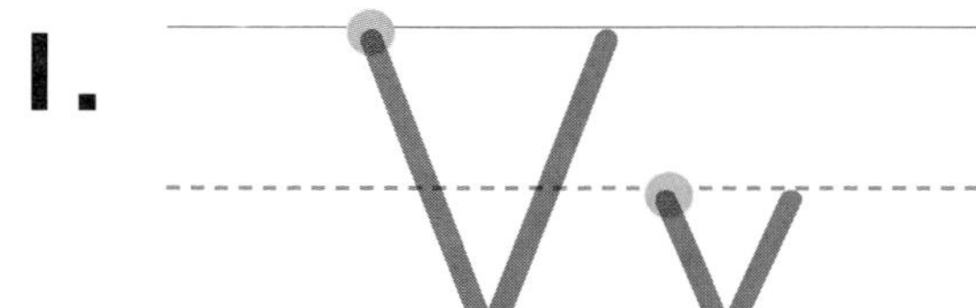

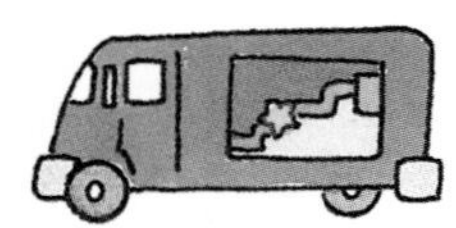

2. 

3.

4.

Write the letters *Vv*. • Say the word that names each picture. • Listen for the sound at the beginning of each word. • Draw a circle around each picture whose name begins with the same sound as *violin*.

Name____

Draw a circle around all the items that belong together. • Cross out the one that does not belong.

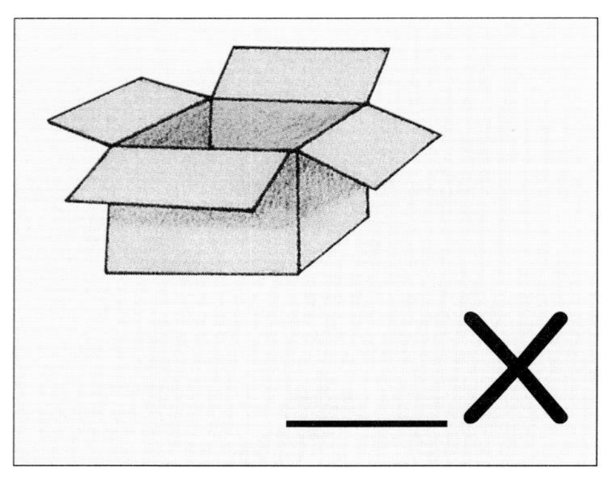

Name ______________________

1.    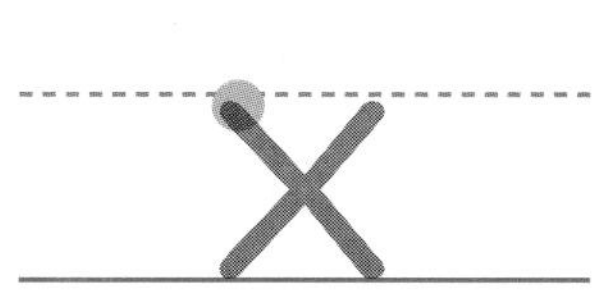

2.    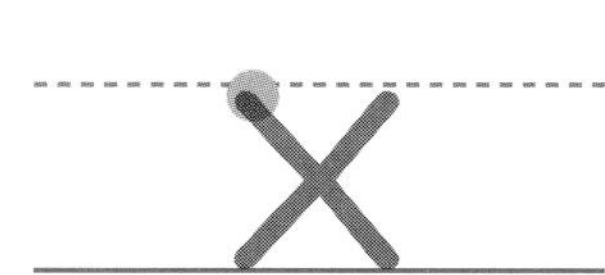

3.  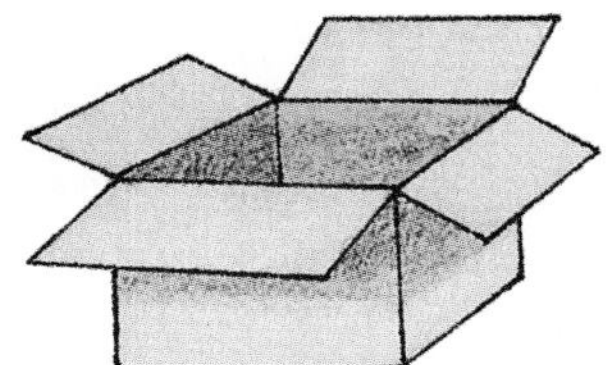 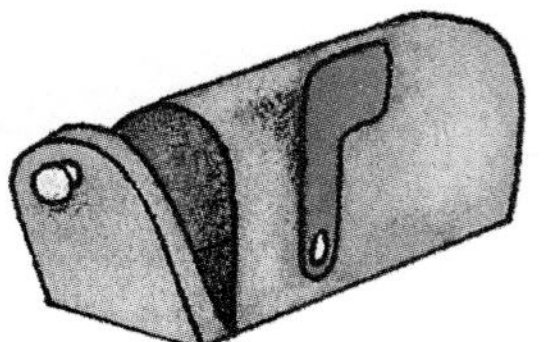 

4. 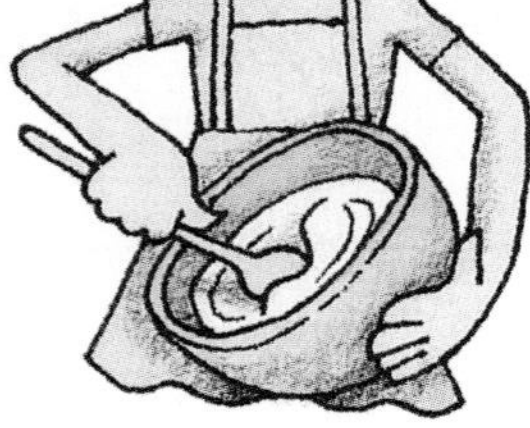  

Say the name of each picture. • Draw a circle around each picture whose name has the same ending sound as *box*. • Write the letter *x*.

Name____

Look at the first picture on the left. The action shown will cause something to happen. Circle one picture in the row that shows what will happen next. Do the same for the rest of the page.

Name

1. 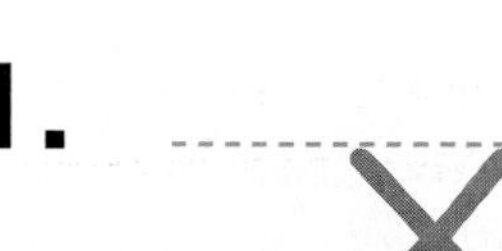

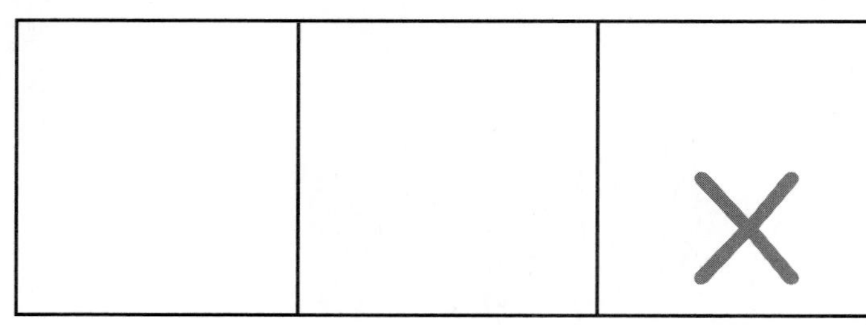

2. 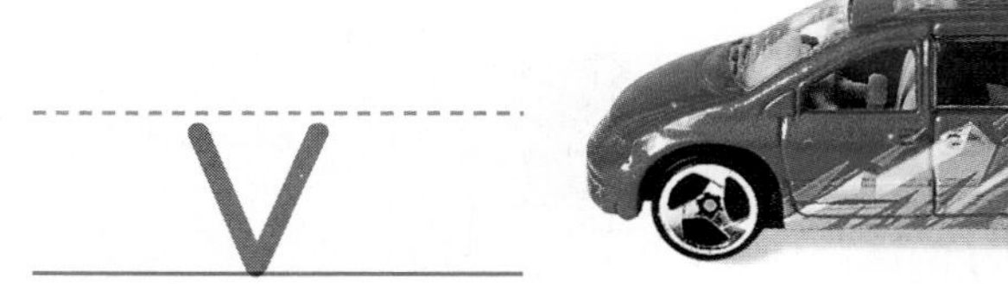

3. 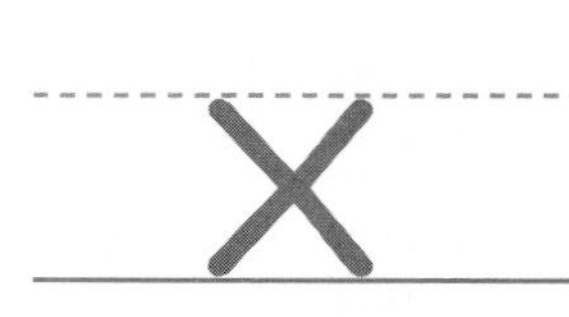
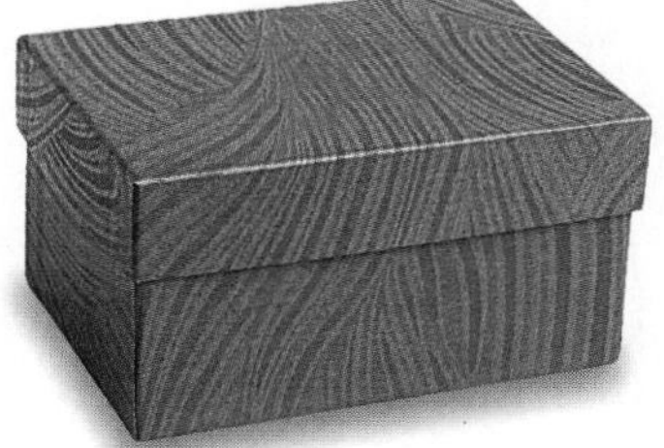

4. 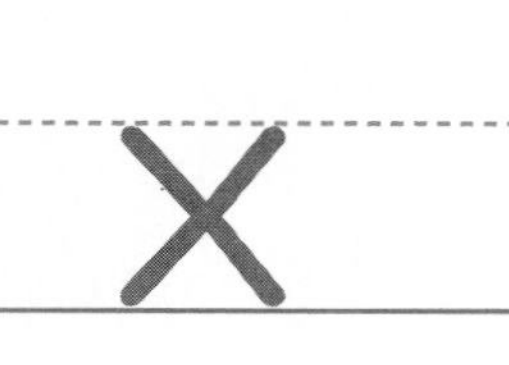

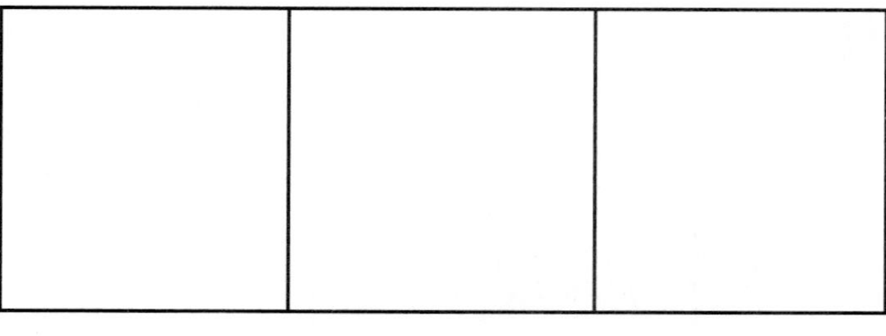

Trace the letter. Say the word that names the picture. Write the letter in the correct box to show if you hear the sound /v/*v* or /ks/*x* at the beginning, middle, or the end of the word.

Name ____________________

1. I can see Dad.

2. Dad can see me.

3. I can see Pup.

4. I can see that Pup is with Dad.

Read the sentences. • Then draw a line under the word *see* in each sentence.

Name

1. o x

ox

2. f a n

3. w e b

4. r u g

Blend the sounds and write the word. Say the word that names the picture.

Rex can go back with Max!

The Vet Van

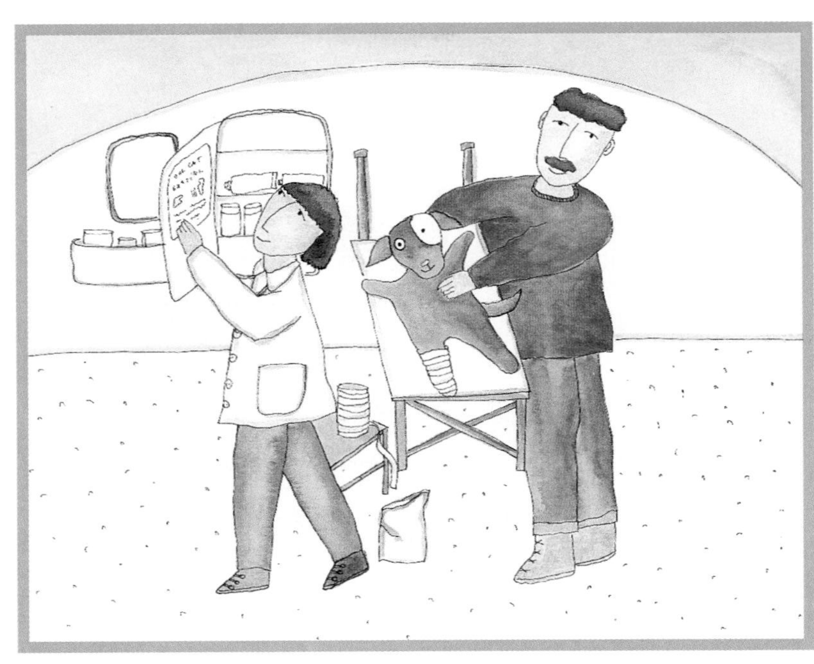

Pam can fix the leg for Rex.

Pam has a van to go see a pet.

Pam is a vet.

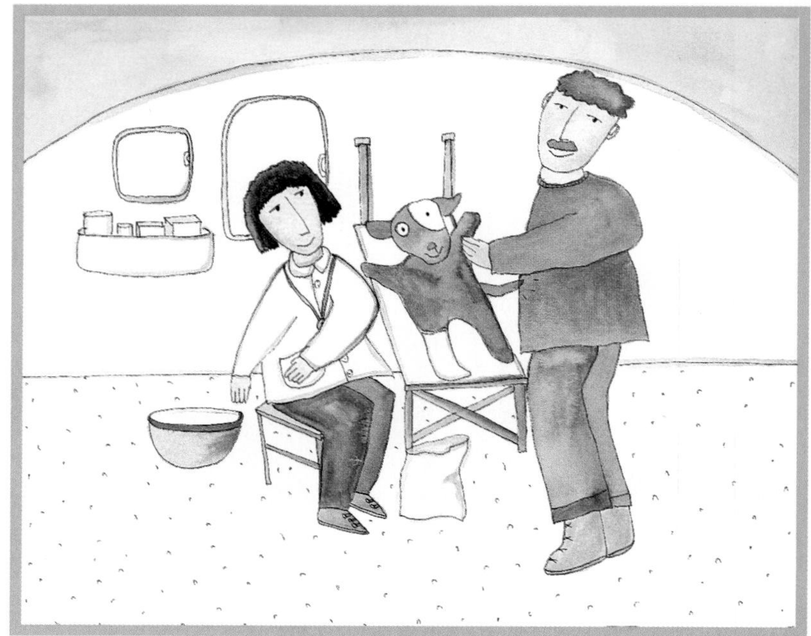

Rex and Max are not sad!

Pam can go for Rex in the van.

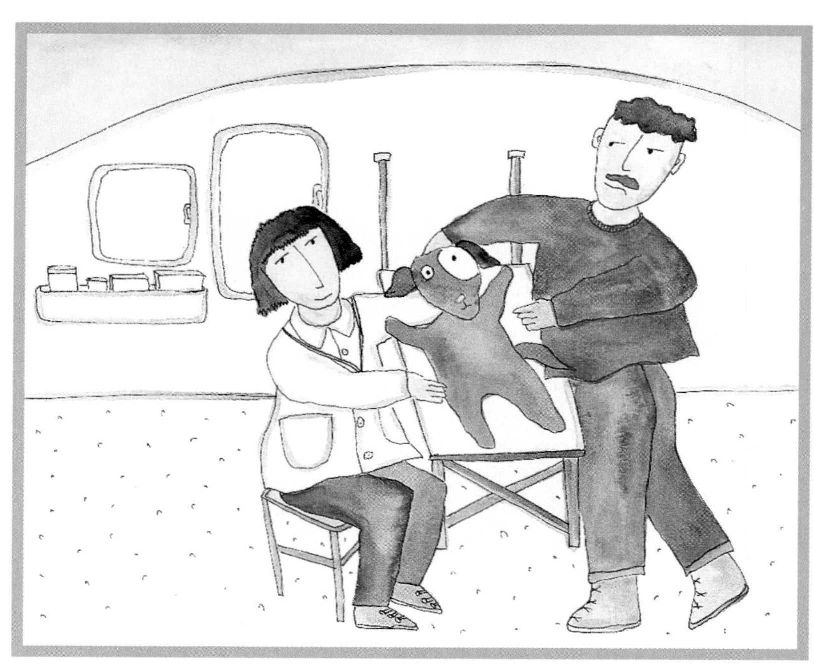

Rex has a bad leg for Pam to see.

Name ______________________________

1. Do you see Ben?

2. We are not with Ben.

3. We can see that Ben was in bed.

4. Ben is sick.

Read each sentence. **1.** Draw a circle around the word *see*. Draw a line under the word *do*. **2.** Draw a circle around the word *are*. Draw a line under the word *we*. Draw two lines under the word *with*. **3.** Draw a circle around the word *we*. Draw a line under the word *was*. **4.** Draw a line under the word *is*.

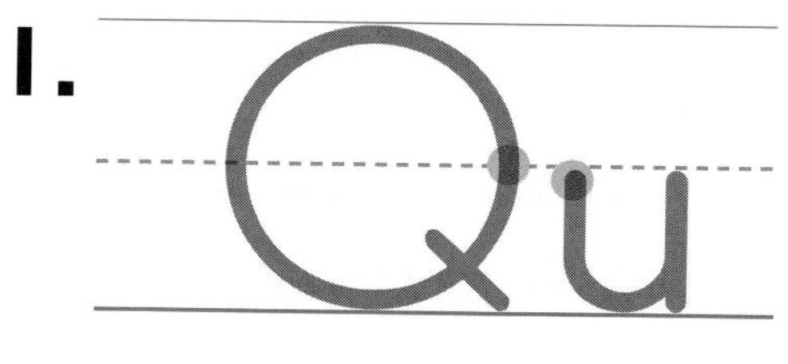

Name____________________________

1. Qu qu

2. Qu qu

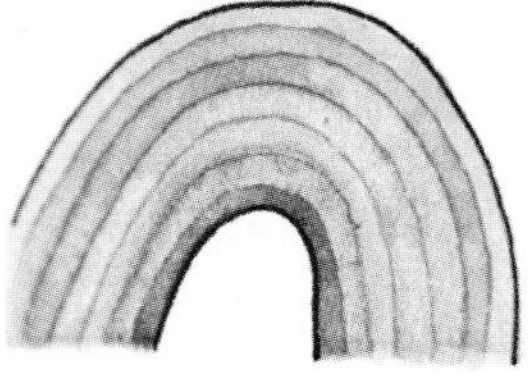

3.

4.

Write the letters *Qu qu*. • Say the word that names each picture. • Listen for the sound at the beginning of each word. • Draw a circle around each picture whose name begins with the same sound as *quilt*.

Name ______________________________

Draw a circle around all the items that belong together. • Cross out the one that does not belong.

Jj

Name________________________________

1. Jj

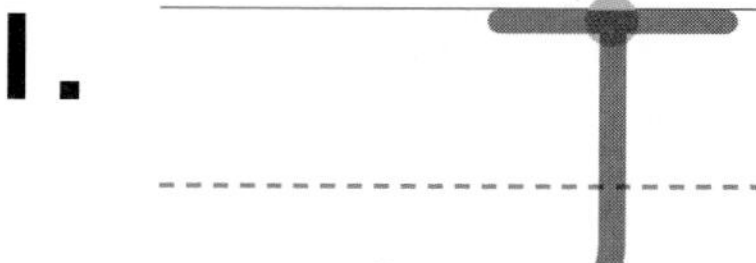

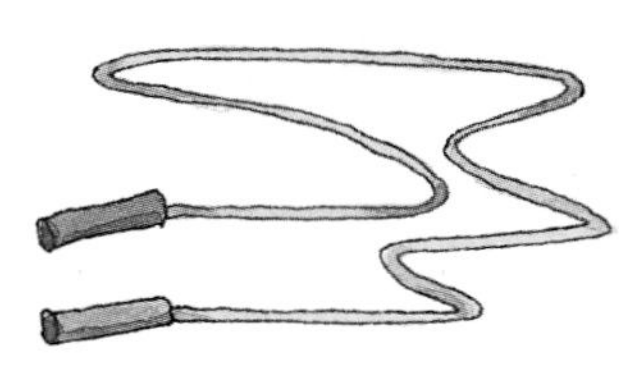

2. Jj

3.

4.

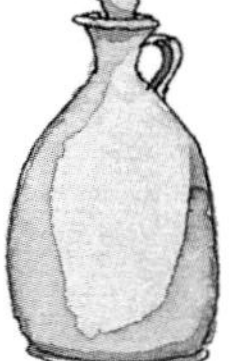

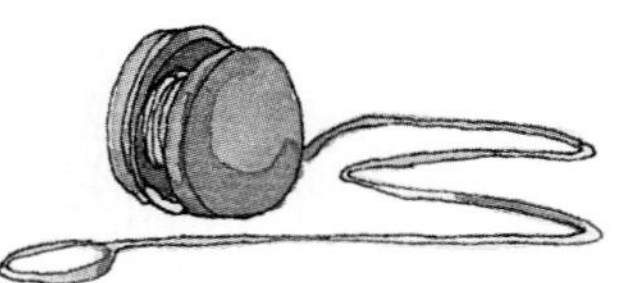

Write the letters *Jj.* • Say the word that names each picture. • Listen for the sound at the beginning of each word. • Draw a circle around each picture whose name begins with the same sound as *jam.*

Name________________________________

1. 

2. 

3. 

Look at the picture on the left. • Draw a circle around the face that shows how the person in the picture is feeling.

Name____________________

1. Yy

2.

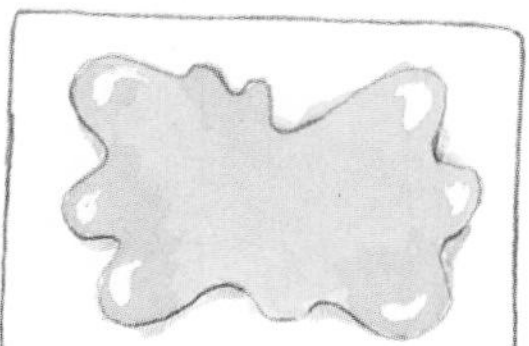

3.

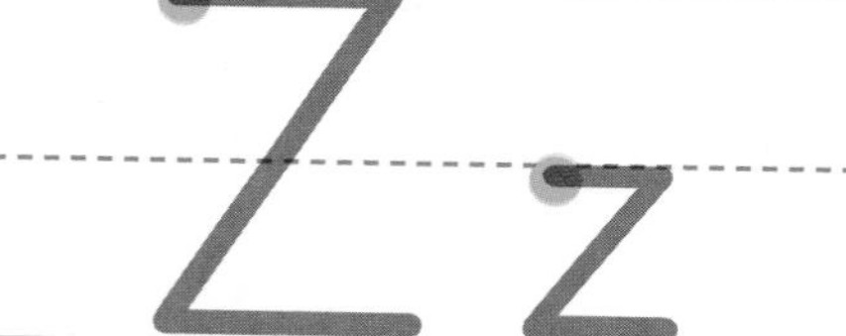

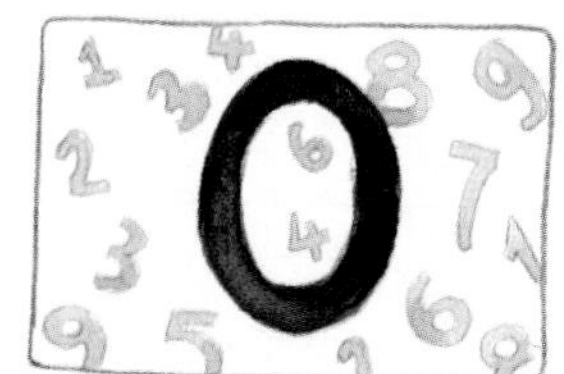

4.

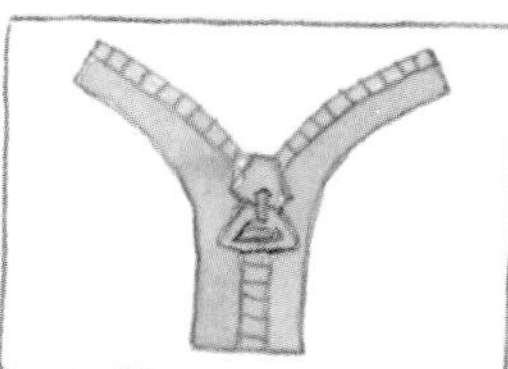
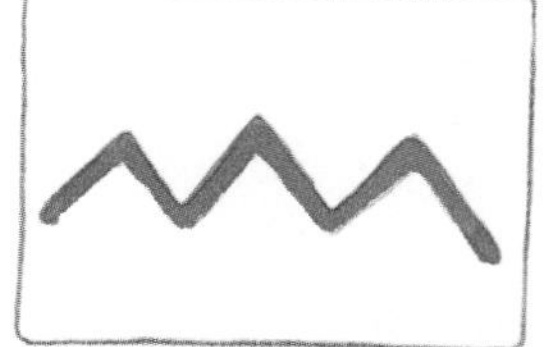

Write the letters *Yy*. • Say the word that names each picture. • Listen for the sound at the beginning of each word. • Draw a circle around each picture whose name begins with the same sound as *yo-yo*. • Do the same with the letters *Zz*. • Draw a circle around each picture whose name begins with the same sound as *zipper*.

Name____________________

of

1\. Jim had a pot of jam.

___

2\. Kim had a tin of ham.

___

3\. I had a mix of ham and yam.

___

4\. We had a lot of fun.

___

Read the sentence. • Then draw a line under the word *of* in the sentence.

Name ____________________

1. j e t

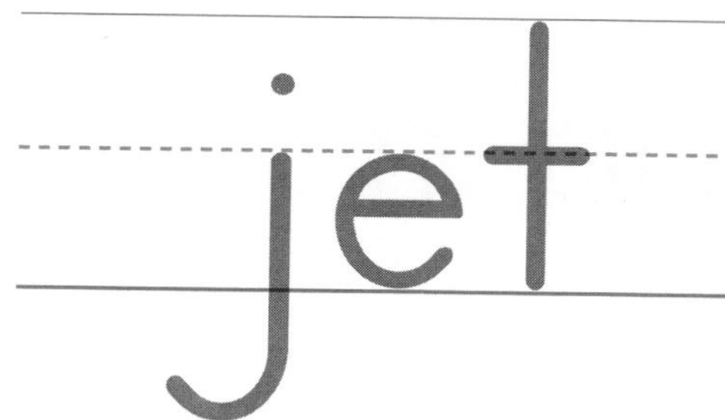

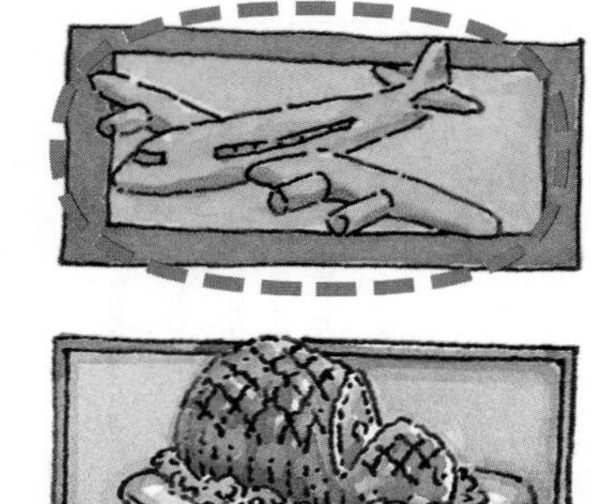

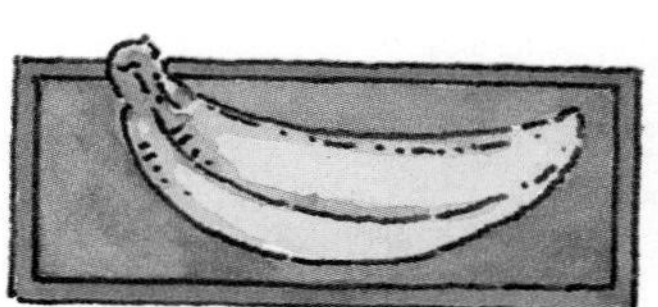

2. y a m

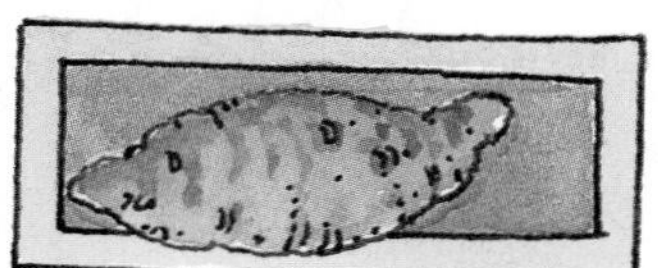

3. z i p

4. qu a ck

Blend the sounds and say the word. • Write the word. • Draw a circle around the picture that goes with the word.

Yip is a quick quack!

Jen and Yip

Jen can zig-zag
with Yip.

Jen can get on top
of a box.

Jen has a pen with a duck and a hen.

2

Jen is quick.

7

Yip can get on top of Jen.

4

Jen can jog to the top of the rock.

5

Name ____

1.

2.

3.

Look at the picture on the left. • Then look at the two pictures on the right. • Draw a line to the picture that shows where the person is going.

Name

1. 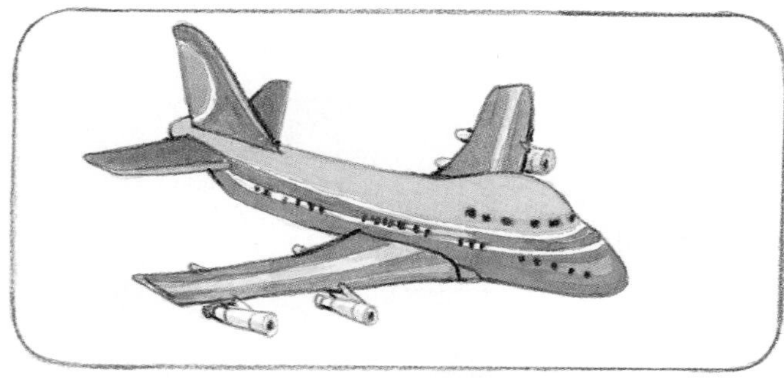

jet job

jet

2. 

quit quack

3. 

yam jam

4. 

jog zip

Draw a circle around the word that names the picture. • Say the word. • Then write the word.

Name ________________________________

1\. Yes, we do have a lot of fun.

2\. I see Rob pick up that sack.

3\. The bug is on the top of my net.

Read each sentence. **1.** Draw a line under the word *of.* **2.** Draw a line under the words *see* and *that.* **3.** Draw a line under the word *my.*

Name________________________________

1. v a n

van

2. h o p

3. m i x

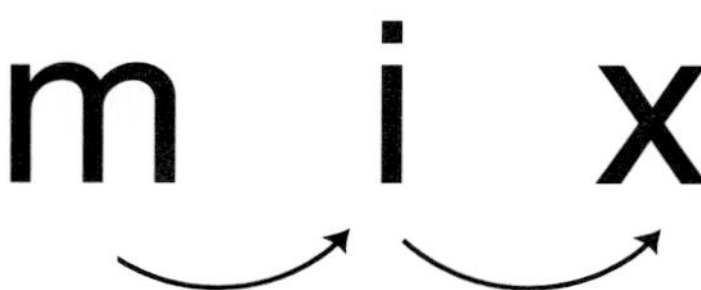

4. w e t

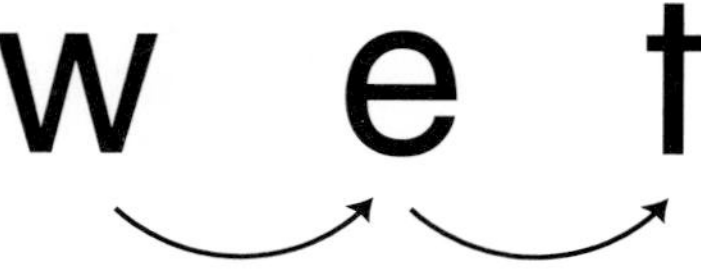

Blend the sounds and say the word. • Write the word. • Draw a circle around the picture that goes with the word.

Name ______________________________

Draw a circle around the animals. • Draw a triangle around the clothing. • Draw a square around the toys.

Name ______________________________

1. j a m

2. y u m

3. z i p

4. qu i ck

Blend the sounds and say the word. • Write the word. • Draw a circle around the picture that goes with the word.

Name ____

Look at the first picture on the left. The action shown will cause something to happen. Circle one picture in the row that shows what will happen next. Do the same for the rest of the page.

Name ____________________

1. 

fan   fox

fox

2. 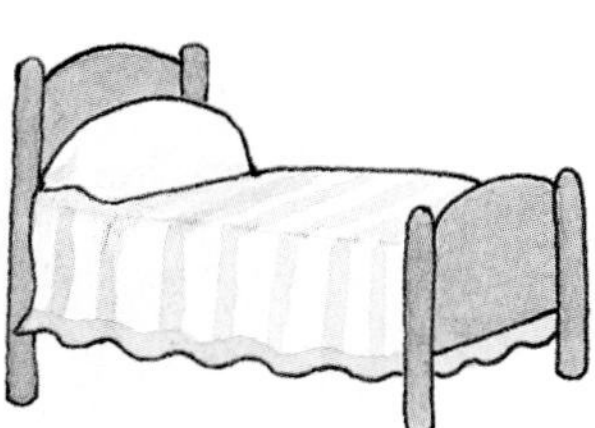

bed   bit

3. 

mad   mud

4. 

jug   jet

Draw a circle around the word that names the picture.
• Say the word. • Then write the word.

Name________________________________

1\. of was see with

2\. was of with see

3\. see with was of

4\. with of see was

Read the four words in each row. **1.** Draw a circle around the word *with.* **2.** Draw a circle around the word *of.* **3.** Draw a circle around the word *was.* **4.** Draw a circle around the word *see.*

Name________________________________

1. 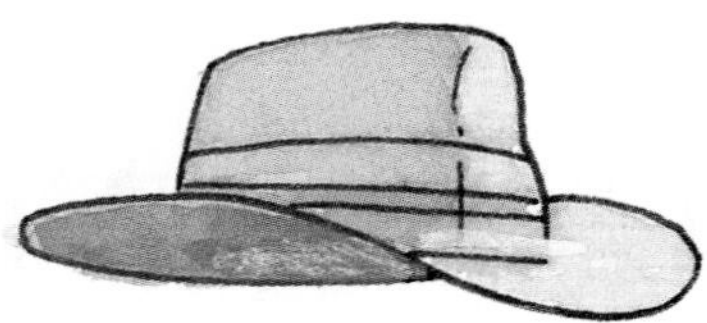

hat hen

hat

2. 

rod rock

3. 

win web

4. 

van vet

Draw a circle around the word that names the picture. • Say the word.
• Then write the word.

"Yum, yum!" said Mom.

Zack and Jan

The van had to zig
and zag.

Jan had a pot of jam
in a big box.

Zack had a tin of ham.

Mom sees Zack and Jan with a big box.

The box with the jam and ham is for Mom.

"We can go in my van," said Jan.

Name ____________________

1.

2.

3.

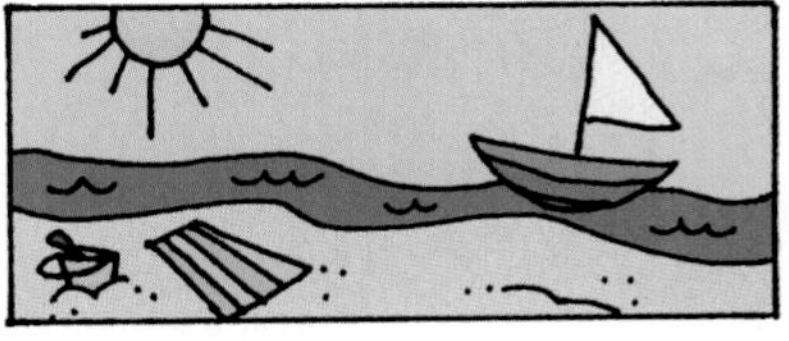

Look at the picture on the left. • Then look at the two pictures on the right. • Draw a line to the picture that shows where the person is going.

Name

1. 

ten six

six

2. 

bug bag

3. 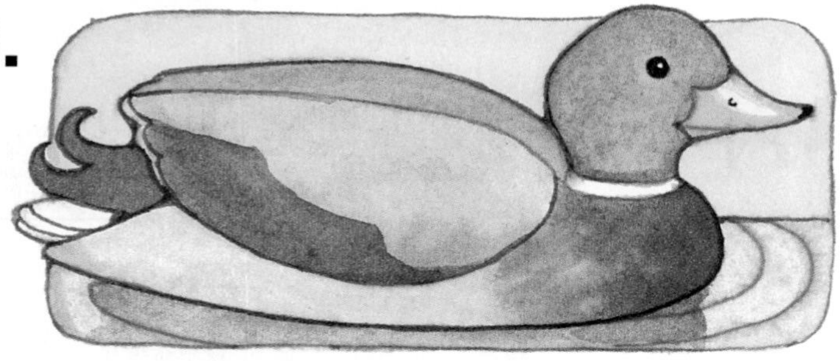

duck dot

4. 

map men

Draw a circle around the word that names the picture. • Say the word. • Then write the word.

Name ________________________________

1. was	are	I	we	was
2. of	do	he	of	for
3. with	have	said	that	with
4. see	the	see	and	you

Say the first word in the row. Draw a circle around the word where you see it in the same row.

Credits

Photos and illustrations are provided by Taurins Design Associates for Macmillan/McGraw-Hill:

Photo Credits

Ken Karp Photography, 7, 44, 46, 56, 58, 60, 70, 80, 87, 94, 105, 106, 118, 130, 154, 178, 187, 202, 214, 226, 236, 238, 250, 259, 262, 272, 274, 286, 298, 310, 322, 334; **Ron Kimbal Photography,** 44, 56, 58, 70, 80, 105, 106, 118, 130, 214, 250, 259, 262, 272 **Animals Animals: Michael Gadomski,** 56; **Ted Levi,** 56, 80; **C. C. Lockwood,** 58, 94; **D. Fleetham,** 60; **John East Cock & Yva Momatiuk,** 80; **Len Rue Jr.,** 154, 322, 334; **Gordan & Cathy Illg,** 154; **John Lemkar,** 286; **R. Dowling,** 310; **CORBIS: Dave G. Houser,** 154; **PhotoDisc: Jules Frazier,** 178, 334; **PhotoDisc: Siede Preis,** 272; **PhotoDisc: C Squared Studios,** 44.

Illustration Credits

Cover Illustration by Steve Sullivan

Diana Craft, 6, 10, 12, 20, 24, 31, 43, 67, 211; **Georgia Cawley,** 7, 84, 151, 159, 211, 241, 242; **Steve Sullivan,** 8, 15, 16, 18, 22, 28, 39; **Joe & Terri Chicko,** 9, 153, 177, 199, 201, 207; **Dorothy Stott,** 21, 33, 45, 51, 57, 297; **Mike Dammer,** 34, 42, 63, 69, 72, 75, 102, 141, 147, 171, 183, 249, 261, 285, 291, 303, 309; **Sally Jo Vitsky,** 48, 52, 64, 82, 165, 190, 336; **Jill Newton,** 93, 349, 350; **Rita Lascaro,** 116, 188, 200, 212, 258, 284, 308, 320; **Cathy Johnson,** 129, 135, 255, 273, 279; **Martha Aviles,** 157, 158; **Ronnie Rooney,** 181, 182; **Jamie Smith,** 205, 206; **Kathi Ember,** 217, 218; **Joe Boddy,** 247, 313, 314, 315, 333, 339, 357; **Keiko Motoyama,** 265, 266, 267.

All other illustrations are provided by the Kirchoff/Wohlberg Company for Macmillan/McGraw-Hill.

Acknowledgments

ZB Font Method Copyright © 1996 Zaner–Bloser. Manuscript handwriting models. Used by permission.